PELICAN
A410
THE BAD
ERNEST N

THE BADGER

ERNEST NEAL

500
NE

PENGUIN BOOKS

Penguin Books Ltd, Harmondsworth, Middlesex

U.S.A.: Penguin Books Inc., 3300 Clipper Mill Road, Baltimore 11, Md

AUSTRALIA: Penguin Books Pty Ltd, 762 Whitehorse Road,
Mitcham, Victoria

—

First published by Collins in the
New Naturalist Monograph series 1948

Published in Pelican Books 1958

Made and printed in Great Britain
by Spottiswoode, Ballantyne & Co Ltd,
London and Colchester

*This book is dedicated to the
badgers of Conigre Wood who suffered my
intrusions into their private lives
with the stoical indifference
of their race*

CONTENTS

CONTENTS

LIST OF PLATES

The photographs for Plates 1, 3, 4, 6, 7, 10, 13, 14, 15, 16, 17, 22, and 23 were taken by the author, for Plate 2 by Aerofilms Ltd, for Plates 5, 8, 9, and 25 by Harold Platt, for Plates 11, 12, 18, 24, 28, and 29 by Arthur Brook, for Plates 20, 21, and 27 by T. Ormsby Ruttledge, and for Plate 26 by A. R. Thompson.

DIAGRAMS

EDITORS' PREFACE

In introducing this book, the editors note with pride that it is written by an amateur English naturalist, about a very widespread, typical, and important British mammal – a mammal which, though so widespread and so important, has been relatively little studied.

It is surprising how few scientific investigations have been made of the life and habits of the badger. All but one or two previous studies have been uncritical and superficial. This is certainly due, in part, to the fact that the badger is nocturnal, and that the badger-watcher has to work inconvenient hours, often in great discomfort.

Mr Neal has probably studied wild badgers more than any living man; he has put in a number of hours in the field that is unique. As a photographer of badgers, he has followed in the paths pioneered by Mr Arthur Brook, some of whose classic photographs of the badger grace this book. He has not wasted his time. He would be the first, we know, to admit that there are many questions about the badger that still remain unsolved; but the results of his researches are such that we at last have a really accurate picture of the year-cycle of this secretive animal, of its habits through the seasons, of its reproduction and family life, of its play and defence and attack. We now know, quite certainly, the badger's gestation period, and can understand the problem of delayed implantation of its foetus. We know a good deal more than we did – though not yet enough! – about what the badger eats.

Mr Neal's careful and devoted work, with his interesting study of badger population, family numbers, distribution of sets, and 'visiting', as well as his research into reproduction and foraging, is an example to British naturalists. It shows just what an informed and critical man, working in his normal occupation in the country – Mr Neal is a schoolmaster – can do with a determined use of limited leisure. Throughout Britain there are other interesting species of animals and plants demanding similar attention; we expect that many amateur naturalists will try to take a leaf out of Mr Neal's book, and emulate his precision and scholarship. There is a subtle satisfaction about the thorough and exclusive study of a single

species – a satisfaction that Mr Neal has succeeded well in convey-
ing to his readers. We are sure that his *Badger* monograph will have
a great success.

JAMES FISHER
JOHN GILMOUR
JULIAN HUXLEY
L. DUDLEY STAMP
ERIC HOSKING

*Every care has been taken by the editors to ensure the scientific accuracy of
factual statements, but the sole responsibility for the interpretation of facts
rests with the author*

AUTHOR'S PREFACE

THE badger (*Meles meles* L.) is one of the largest of our British mammals and one of the wildest members of our fauna. Long before Britain was an island, the badger was here, foraging among the acorns of the great oak forest of the south with tireless energy and excavating its remarkable underground sets.

Much has been written about the badger by naturalists and sportsmen, and many a tale told over a mug of ale of its prowess against the terriers of the 'locals'. But, in spite of good observations by many, its life is still shrouded in mystery, and less is known of its habits than of those of any other of our larger mammals.

The literature on the subject abounds with conflicting theories, and many of the statements found about the badger's habits are based on incomplete evidence and even guess-work. On the one hand we read that the badger is a destroyer of poultry and will kill lambs; on the other that it is mainly vegetarian, varying its diet with insects and earthworms. One authority states that it hibernates, another holds the opposite view. Its time of mating has been the subject for debate for generations, and almost every month from February to October has been suggested as a probable time. Its period of gestation has varied from nine weeks to fifteen months according to various theorists, but, now the problem has been solved, the solution is more intriguing than most of us imagined.

Of course, badgers are extremely difficult to observe under natural conditions for good reasons. They are fairly strictly nocturnal, emerging from their sets after darkness has fallen except during the summer months when the shorter nights bring them out at dusk. During the day they are safe from all observations, lying curled up in a comfortable bed of leaves in some corner of their underground home. Since they are such shy animals, you seldom come across them as you do foxes, and in the daytime there is little to catch the eye of the casual observer save the enormous mounds of earth outside the sets. No wonder the evidence is so circumstantial and conflicting.

This book tells of an attempt to solve the major problems of the badger's life history, using new methods of observation. It is also an attempt to sort out the facts for which there is adequate evidence from the welter of hypotheses.

I have watched badgers in their natural surroundings on many more than one hundred occasions, but it still gives me intense pleasure and a feeling of excited anticipation when I see that first glimpse of a striped face at the set entrance. The more I get to know these grand animals the more fascinating I find them.

It was not long before I came up against observation difficulties. I would go up to the wood one night and watch the badgers at their set, but soon they would wander off, perhaps not to return before dawn. Following them was wellnigh impossible. Where did they go? What did they do? The next night I would go to the same set but not a badger would I see. Were they still there? Had they sensed my presence and decided to remain at home, or had they decamped to another set not far off? The only way of solving the problem was to be in a number of places at the same time, for in this wood alone there were five separate sets spread over an area of a few acres. This difficulty, insurmountable on my own, was solved with the help of several senior biology students at Rendcomb College where I was teaching. One was posted near each set, and each kept a record of what happened and when. In this way a much more complete picture was obtained of the badgers in that woodland community, and it was possible to get an exact knowledge of the number of badgers there, and their movements during the early part of the night. This method was developed over several years of intensive observations.

At first the badgers were exceedingly wary, but as time went on our woodcraft and technique improved and the animals became more used to the scent of man round their sets. As they were never harmed under these conditions they began to tolerate our presence more easily and would emerge from their sets unless scent was strong or we moved carelessly. By correlating the results of our observations with those obtained during regular visits to all the sets during the daytime, a fairly complete picture was built up of their seasonal movements, activities, and life history.

I would like to acknowledge gratefully the enthusiastic help given me from time to time in my observations by students of Rendcomb College, including the following: Messrs R. Brain, M. Butler, J. E. Carus-Wilson, D. M. Grant, S. H. Groves, D. H. Hill, I. S. Menzies, S. North, H. S. Palmer, and R. Wood; also Miss Anne Gladstone. Whenever there was a count to be done under good or bad conditions there was never a lack of enthusiastic cooperation.

I should also like to thank Dr L. Harrison Matthews for much help and advice: also the numerous correspondents who have supplied data from other parts of the country; their names will appear in the text. I am also indebted to the Ministry of Agriculture for certain facts concerning the distribution of the badger in England and Wales. Finally I must record my indebtedness to Mr James Fisher for much advice and kindly criticism.

ERNEST NEAL

Foxcombe,
Greenway Road,
Taunton.

CHAPTER I

THE BADGER AT HOME

No naturalist who has once watched badgers is ever content with that one experience: he wants to go again and again. There is something about badger-watching that draws you on in spite of cold feet or a series of blank nights. Let me try and describe a typical evening.

It is June, and as the sun sinks towards the horizon we note the way of the wind with some care – as that will determine what set to watch, our method of approach, and choice of vantage point. It will mean a walk of about a mile over rough hill pasture. The grass is long and rank; and we find it less tiring if we keep to the rabbit tracks which wind about among the ant hills. We have a torch with us, as on the way back we want to avoid the leaves of the woolly thistle, which can be most unpleasant in the dark. As we approach a grassy mound a hare darts away and gallops off in a wide arc, poising once on the edge of the hill with ears erect to watch our movements.

Patches of woodland dot this Cotswold country, and it is towards one of these that we are making our way. Crawling through some awkward barbed wire, we skirt one strip of wood until we come to a steep bank on our left. Brambles are growing in profusion, and a few untidy elders screen our view. Halfway up the bank is an enormous heap of earth. It looks as if cart after cart had dumped their loads of clay over the bank. No cart, however, has been near; it is the work of badgers. Generations of these industrious beasts have been at work excavating the hillside and piling the unwanted clay outside their set.

We have to move very cautiously now as time is getting on and a badger may be near the entrance and sense our presence. The wind is blowing in our faces as we clamber up the bank and climb into a large oak tree. What a help it would be if there were always trees so conveniently placed!

The first thing to do is to get as comfortable as possible; before long we may not have the opportunity to move our limbs at will, and a tree can be a most uncomfortable resting-place after an hour or two.

Looking down, we see that the pile of earth is really a platform trodden flat by the feet of many badgers. It is like looking down from the gallery of a theatre on to the stage below. A gnarled ivy-clad tree grows out from the bank to our right and at its roots gapes a large hole; this is the entrance to the badger stronghold. In this particular set it is the only one, a most unusual thing, as normally there are three or four to a large set, and this one is not small judging by the tons of earth outside. From our point of view this is a good thing because we know that if they come out at all they will have to emerge in front of us.

Behind the set the bank rises steeply; it is studded with projecting roots and has lost most of its vegetation. Two well-worn paths lead away from the platform in opposite directions; they are so plain it is difficult to realize that they were not made by man.

Eagerly we watch the dark entrance of the set for the first glimpse of a badger, but nothing happens. It is not dark enough and we must be patient. A rabbit comes down the bank to our right in a series of short jumps, pausing for a moment with ears erect to see that all is well. It passes the foot of our tree and quickly reaches the grass, where it is joined by others.

A cuckoo flies over to its roosting-tree across the valley, and a magpie lands on our tree with a raucous volley of sound sufficient to scare all the badgers in the district. If a magpie does not notice us a badger certainly will not if the wind is right, so we pride ourselves on having kept so still. The countryside is quieter now and every sound focuses our attention. As we watch the set entrance we hear a low, quavering, yelping sound coming from the depths of the earth. It is rather muffled and indistinct. It is the badgers at last. It cannot be long now before we see something, because that murmuring is a sign of impatience; there are cubs somewhere out of sight and they are eager to come out and play.

The light is not so good now, but from our perch fifteen feet from the set entrance we can still see details quite distinctly. We need not fear being seen as our backs are against the main trunk, and a badger's eyesight is rather poor, but we mustn't move or take liberties of that sort.

Was that something white at the entrance? It looked like it, but it is not there now. Yes it is; a black and white striped face is carefully scenting the air, first in this direction, then in that. We can only see the head at the moment with its tiny white-tipped ears. Bother! It has gone in again. If it has, it will be twenty minutes or so before it tries again. But no, it's coming right out. It is still very suspicious, and, as we hold our breath and watch, it sits there ready at the slightest alarm to dash down its set. Every now and then it raises its pig-like snout to scent the wind, but all is well, and soon it takes less notice of its surroundings and starts to scratch.

No doubt the confines of its underground home make scratching difficult, so it makes up for it now. How it can scratch! It has been said that the badger is the only animal that shares with man the honour of being host to the species of flea known as *Pulex irritans!*

The scratching ceases at last, and the badger has a leisurely look around. It is quite a large animal and obviously an adult. We would guess by its behaviour that it is a male, but there are no distinguishing marks between the sexes visible at that distance.

Slowly it turns towards the set and peers down as if to say, 'What are you waiting for? It's quite all right up here this evening.' Almost immediately another face appears, this time the female. But she does not take anything for granted; her senses, if anything, are better developed than her mate's, and besides she has family worries and dare not take risks. However, the wind tells her of no danger and out she comes. She is smaller and somewhat more sleek, possibly a younger

* Russell (1913).

19

animal than her mate. No sooner is she out of the set than another face appears, this time a little one. Out it comes, followed by another. The two cubs are more fluffy than their parents, and one has a snub nose, giving it the appearance of a teddy bear but coloured like a panda.

The mother at once noses up to them and they remain quite close. Meanwhile the male has wandered off and is now padding slowly down the path to the left towards some bushes twenty or thirty yards away.

One cub has got a stone in its mouth, and it is grumbling hard because it can't break it, but the grumbling ends in a yelp as its mother playfully bites it. She is now going over the fur of the cub with her mouth to remove any parasites that may be there, then with a deft push she sends it rolling upside down on the bare earth. But there is method in her play, because she is at once examining the under-fur to see if it is clean. The examination over, the cub bounds off, and now it is the second cub's turn to be cleaned.

The cubs are now eager for play. One of them comes up behind its mother and surreptitiously nips her; there is a scuffle and soon the three are chasing each other's tails and rolling over and over in their excitement. A moment's pause and then a cub dashes down the set, the other makes to follow, but it's only a game of hide and seek, and out comes the first with a mighty rush knocking the other head over heels.

Suddenly there is a rustle. Instantly all is quiet and the three badgers sit silently listening. The sound is repeated, but this time it fills them with no fear. It is the boar returning. We can just see his face as he comes jog-trotting towards us, and, on reaching the platform, he comes up to the sow and they rub noses together by way of greeting. But the cubs are at it again, tumbling and scuffling with intermittent yelps when one gets hurt rather more than usual. The parents join in, but not for long; without warning one goes pounding off at a headlong rush. The others listen for a moment, and then follow in single file, running hard to catch up.

Play is over. The next item is breakfast. The sounds die away as the badgers get farther off, and we suddenly realize our legs are frightfully cramped. We had forgotten our discomfort in the excitement. They might return, but the hope is not great, so, putting on the torch as it is getting dark now, we carefully climb down the tree.

As we tramp home we wonder what the badger family is doing; are they looking for beetles under the dung in the meadow, or digging for bulbs in the wood, or is the mother teaching her cubs how to find nests of young rabbits? If only we could follow them and see!

It is late when we get home, but it has been a good evening. Now the thought of supper is an attractive one. There is only one question more to be settled that night. When shall we go again?

CHAPTER 2

GENERAL FEATURES

THE European badger (*Meles meles* L., formerly *Meles taxus*) is the only species of badger inhabiting Britain. It has a long, rather wedge-shaped body measuring up to three feet from the tip of the snout to the end of the tail. The tail is stumpy, only about four or four and a half inches long, and usually light in colour. The head is rather short, and when you see a badger emerging from its set you are surprised, after seeing the head, by the size of the body that follows.

The legs of the badger are short; but their strength is out of all proportion to their length. They are very strong indeed. The feet are plantigrade; the animal walks on the flat of its feet including the heel, in contrast to the Ungulates, which walk on their toes. This gives the pad marks of the badger a very characteristic appearance which it is impossible to mistake for the dog-like prints of the fox. In this connexion it is important to note that the print made by the fore foot of a badger is definitely larger than that of the hind; so that the presence of pad marks of two sizes at a set entrance does not necessarily mean that more than one badger has been there.

With a perfect imprint the claw marks can also be seen quite clearly. If, then, pad marks are seen in the clay at the mouth of a large hole, the presence of the five toe marks points with certainty to the badger. The width of the prints is a good indication of the size of the badger. For example, a large male would have a width of five centimetres for the fore foot and four and a half for the hind; while a large female would have four and a half for the fore and four for the hind. When a badger is running the hind feet overlap the fore feet slightly, but, near the set, where its movements are slower and less characteristic, this is not always the case. It is difficult under these circumstances to decide which mark is made by the fore limb and which by the hind. One difference is that the claw marks are usually much larger and better defined in the fore foot, and the big toe is relatively farther back than in the hind foot.

The claws of the fore feet are very large, an essential adaptation for digging; and often they are very sharp. They cannot, of course, be contracted like a cat's. In old specimens the claws of the hind feet are often much worn by the con-

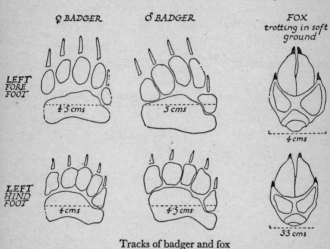

Tracks of badger and fox

stant digging. One old male I examined had them almost worn away, though the claws of its front feet were in good condition.

Badgers are very heavy creatures, surprisingly so for their length. In the Cotswolds I should say the average weight of an adult male is about twenty-seven pounds, and that of the female a few pounds lighter. A badger of forty-three pounds was recorded by R. A. Swayne (1908). There are a number of other records of badgers over forty pounds including one from Owen Mansell in the *Field* of a boar which weighed forty-two pounds, and a sow of thirty-eight. This was on 5 March 1921, a time of year when badgers are usually at their lightest. Gwion Davies (1936) also mentions a forty-two-pound badger which was shot and weighed by Mr Roger Williams of Llansannan in Denbighshire.

Although there are no figures to go upon, Mortimer Batten (1923) is convinced that the Highland badgers go heavier; he cites several keepers who know both Lowland and Highland races, and who are convinced that a large Lowland badger is equal only to a medium mountain form. Estimates of from forty-five to fifty pounds have been made; I am disappointed in being unable to find any accurate measurements.

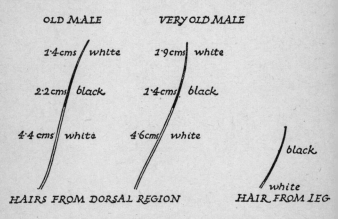

OLD MALE   VERY OLD MALE

1·4 cms / white   1·9 cms white

2·2 cms black   1·4 cms black

4·4 cms white   4·6 cms white

black

white

HAIRS FROM DORSAL REGION   HAIR FROM LEG

The colouring of the badger is of considerable interest. Most specimens look grey from a distance, though there is a lot of variation. The greyness is due to the hairs, which are individually part black, part white. The lighter portion is nearest the skin; then comes a region of black, sometimes tailing off to brown at both ends; the distal region is again white. This would be typical for a hair taken from a normal badger in the dorsal region. The lower surfaces of the animal are, however, much darker, though the hairs in this region are not so thick. The hairs on the leg are almost entirely black, except perhaps for a very short region of white just at the base. The hairs on the head are white, as also are those from

24

the side of the neck; but two black stripes of hairs break the pattern up and help to reduce the conspicuousness of the eyes. The ears are tiny and tipped with white.

In diurnal animals the upper parts are darker than the under, which produces an appearance of flatness and tone-similarity against the background, when light rays of varying intensity strike the animal. That is why a rabbit, when alive, is so inconspicuous against a dull background, but when shot lies on its side and shows up clearly.

With some nocturnal animals, including the badger, the opposite is true, and the lighter colour above and the darker below help to make it more conspicuous than otherwise. But what of a badger's head? Could anything be more conspicuous? When I first watched them I thought that this black and white striping had something to do with patches of moonlight coming through the trees and was protective. Mortimer Batten makes out a case for this in his book on the badger, but I am now convinced that this is not so. On the whole, badgers dislike strong moonlight, but when I have seen them under these circumstances they stand out distinctly against any background. When a badger is difficult to see, no other British mammal could be seen at all. When there is just enough light to see a fox or a rabbit, a badger's head is as plain as a white flag.

No. Some other explanation is necessary for this distinctive pattern. For this we turn to a most interesting paper by Pocock (1911), who collected much information about the habits of animals which had this striking black and white colouring. He found that they were on the whole fearless creatures with some effective defence mechanism – either a tremendous bite like the badger, or a powerful nauseating odour like the skunk. They were all either nocturnal or crepuscular, and fed on small animals, including insects and land molluscs – animals that would not get away in a hurry. They moved noisily, advertising their presence to all who came near. They were not aggressive unless attacked, preferring to go about their own business and leaving others to theirs. Now these generalizations are true for the majority of animals coloured in this way, and it appears to be a type of warning colouration best seen at night – a warning to keep off or there will be trouble. This explanation I heartily endorse, as it certainly sums up very well the behaviour of a badger as I have noted it. It is much more convincing than the protective-resemblance theory for which there is so little evidence. This explanation, however, may not be the complete answer, as this type of coloration may well serve for recognition between members of the same species, especially in the darkness of their underground tunnels. But it is my opinion that recognition is not the sole use of this coloration, and that Pocock was right in attributing it, at any rate in part, to warning coloration.

There is some variation in the colour of badgers. It is noticeable that some are much greyer than others, and some may be described as really silvery. It is possible that this is not attributable to old age, but I have some evidence that it often is. First of all, I have never known any really silvery cubs; they are usually grey, but not the silvery grey of some adults. I have known, however, a number of adults of that colour. There was one very large boar that lived in Conigre Wood that I could recognize with ease because it was nearly white. It was certainly the largest badger living in that community and therefore probably one of the oldest. Then, if you examine the individual hairs of badgers, the proportion of white to black is greater in older specimens. I have specimens of hair from the dorsal region of badgers which I have examined, and in which I have compared this proportion of white to black with the weight of the thymus gland (which gets smaller with age), the wearing of the teeth, and the condition of the claws of the hind feet. So far all the data point to the conclusion that increased whiteness of the hairs is a characteristic of age.

Occasionally badgers have very black coats, especially as cubs. In 1944 there was a cub in Conigre with a coat like black velvet. I was fortunate enough to be able to photograph it as it left the set, on the same occasion as I photographed a cub of similar age which was coloured normally. As both

were in the same position, taken under exactly similar circumstances, developed at the same time, and printed on
similar paper, the contrast between the two is remarkable.
Some white can be made out in the dark one, so it is not a
true melanic variety, but it approaches this condition.

Albinos are not extremely rare. They are pure white, or
slightly yellow like a ferret, and have the usual pink eyes.

A more usual variation is the erythristic form, where the
parts normally black are replaced by a sandy red, so there is
no black pigment at all in the fur. A fine specimen of this
type is to be found in the Taunton Museum; it was captured
on the Blackdown hills. This variation has been reported
from a number of counties.

A yellowish form is also known to occur fairly commonly,
but this colouring as a rule is not very pronounced. Many
allusions have been made to this form, and several explanations have been put forward as to why its colour is yellow.
It is thought by some that the colour is due to the badgers
living in sets which pass through layers of sandy soil, which
after years contaminate the coats sufficiently to make a permanent yellow tint. This seems to me to be most unlikely, as
not all the badgers of the same set are similar in colour, and
young and old have the same characteristics. A temporary
colour may well be attributed to a bout of digging in sandy
soil, but it is quickly removed, as the badger is very particular
with its toilet.

Another theory is that yellow colour is a result of old age;
but it is admitted that old badgers often have no yellow colour
and young ones sometimes do, so that also is not a likely explanation. A clue to the solution (in my opinion) was given
by a fortunate occurrence in Conigre Wood during 1945. We
were having a count at two sets in the wood on 1 May. At
one set a family emerged in good light and played about for
quite a long time before dispersing: there were the father,
mother, and two small cubs. Their colouring was typical. At
the other set Stuart Groves gave me the following account.
He saw three adults, one emerging late, and four cubs; the
latter were all small, but two were smaller than the others,

and to his surprise were sandy-coloured. The others were normally coloured. The sandy ones were no bigger than large rabbits and were romping with the rest, coming on several occasions to within a yard of his feet in good light. There were several possible explanations of this. As one boar had been trapped in March, it was known that one female, probably with cubs, was without a mate. So he might have been watching two families. The cubs might have been two and two, three and one, or even four and none if no cubs had been born to one pair. The likely explanation in terms of size and colour were two and two. This was later found to be the case when the families separated. A few weeks later I saw the sow and her two cubs at the set where the boar had previously been trapped; no other badgers were present. I came upon them in broad daylight and I could see the colours perfectly. The cubs were markedly yellow, but it was the mother that caught my eye; she was bright sandy yellow, the colour of those rabbits seen (occasionally) in a large warren, more yellow than a sandy cat. This family was so unlike the rest of the badgers in Conigre that it gave me a unique opportunity of tracing the movements of a family through the year.

On the same night both the other families were seen at another set, four adults and four cubs, so I had more confirmation that I was watching the sow that had lost her mate.

I examined the skin of the trapped male and was interested to note that it also showed distinct signs of yellowness, but nothing like the colour of the female. Her colour was so bright that there was no possibility of it being due to the earth she had been digging in. It was also in her cubs, but not in any other cubs living in the same wood on similar calcareous soil. This pointed very strongly to a hereditary character, and I have no doubt in my own mind that permanent yellowness is a heritable factor. But if yellowness to some degree is common (as it certainly is in the Cotswolds and in Somerset in my experience – and elsewhere too, according to reports), and if it were due to a *single* recessive character, we would expect more of the bright-yellow forms to turn up. But I have only seen this one, and have not read of any other. It is my belief that hair colour is probably not inherited simply, but is controlled by one or more series of multiple allelomorphs,* and only when all 'yellow' factors are passed on together does the full degree of yellowness show. Unfortunately, only breeding experiments would prove the point, and in practice they would be very difficult to carry out, so all I can do is to suggest this as a possible explanation.

A detailed description of the internal anatomy of the badger would be out of place in this book, but I would like to refer to a few features of general interest. Badgers are

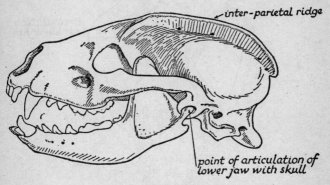

Skull of male badger

notoriously difficult to kill, and there are a number of local stories to illustrate the point. It is said that it is quite useless hitting them over the head with a club or the butt of a gun, they will just shake their heads and go off. The stories become elaborated when the contents of both barrels from a shot gun are poured into the poor animal with little effect. The truth behind these yarns is probably the extraordinary growth of the inter-parietal ridge of bone on the dorsal surface of the skull in the mid line; this takes off the blow from the main surface of the skull. This ridge is half an inch deep in places and really serves for the attachment of the great jaw

* For an explanation of this term, see Appendix, p. 171.

muscles that are highly developed in the badger. However, a comparatively slight tap on the nose of the animal will cause its death, as this point has little protection.

Another feature of interest in the skull is the articulation of the lower jaw. The latter fits into a groove in such a

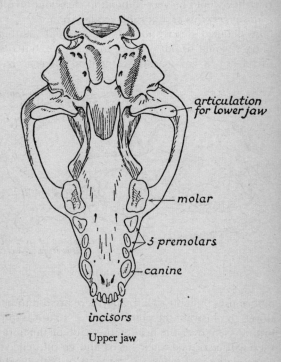

Upper jaw

complete manner that it will not dislocate; if it comes away at all the skull will be fractured.

The dentition is carnivore in type, but has certain modifications which point to the badger's more omnivorous habits; for instance, the molars are considerably flattened to facilitate the grinding-up of vegetable food although the canine teeth are prominent. The carnassial tooth is not such a conspicuous feature as it is in the fox and other exclusively flesh-eating carnivora. The dental formula is usually given thus:

$$2 \left\{ \frac{\text{Incisors } 3 \ : \ \text{Canines } 1 \ : \ \text{Premolars } 3 \ : \ \text{Molars } 3}{3 \ : \quad\quad 1 \ : \quad\quad\quad 3 \ : \quad\quad\quad 2} \right\}$$

This, however, is not quite accurate, as on close examination it is found that in the lower jaw there is a tiny vestigial

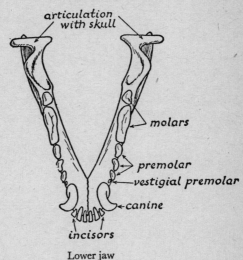

Lower jaw

premolar just behind each canine, making the true dental formula:

$$2 \left\{ \frac{3 \ : \ 1 \ : \ 3 \ : \ 1}{3 \ : \ 1 \ : \ 4 \ : \ 2} \right\}$$

In the Mustelidae, the family to which the badger belongs, there is an interesting reduction in number of the premolars. The genus *Mustela*, which includes the polecat, has the full number – four premolars, upper and lower. Then there is the badger with one upper premolar less and the corresponding lower one vestigial. But in a subspecies of the badger found in Siberia called *Meles meles leptorhynchus* this vestigial tooth is completely absent in the adult. In this way it resembles the genus *Mydaus*, to which the Teledu* belongs. Some of the skunks of the genus *Mephitis* show a further reduction.

In the badger the adaptation to a more omnivorous diet is also reflected in the length of the intestine, which proportionally is much longer than that of the fox.

* See next chapter.

CHAPTER 3

CLASSIFICATION & DISTRIBUTION

THE badgers of the world are included in the sub-family
Melinae of the family Mustelidae. There are six recognized
genera in the Melinae, as follows:

The first genus, *Meles*, contains four species, all of which are
to be found in Europe and Asia. In this genus the nose is
not grooved, the soles of the feet are naked, and the claws
of the hind feet are much smaller than those of the fore
feet. The dentition, as described on p. 30, is typical. One
species, *M. anakuma*, is confined to Japan, while *M. leucurus*
is found in China and Tibet. *M. albogularis* is also found in
the latter country. The distribution of the type species *M.
meles* is described fully later.

The second genus, *Arctonyx*, includes the Sand- or Hog-
badgers of Asia. There are three species: *A. collaris* is to be
found from Nepal to Assam, and in Arakan, Burma, and
Central Borneo. *A. taxoides* also inhabits Assam, Arakan,
and Burma; while *A. leucolaimus* occurs in Central China
and Mongolia. The Hog-badger has a long mobile and
truncated snout with terminal nostrils. Part of its palate is
formed from the pterygoid bones, a characteristic of whales
and certain Edentates. It lives in holes dug by itself or in
fissures of rocks.

The third genus, *Mydaus*, includes the Teledu or Stinking
badger (*M. meliceps*). It is much more of a burrower than
Meles, spending much time burrowing after worms and
larvae. For this it is well adapted, having a long snout and
elongated body, rudimentary tail, and ears hidden by the
fur. Also the toes of the fore paws are united together as far
as the roots of the long, sharp claws. The fur is uniformly
brown except for a white stripe which runs from the head

right along the dorsal mid-line to the root of the tail. It is a small badger and is to be found above six thousand feet on the mountains of Java and Sumatra. A second species, *M. marchei*, is found in the Philippines.

The fourth genus, *Taxidea*, includes the American badgers with *Taxidea taxus* as type. This is a smaller badger than our European type and is to be found almost wholly in the open sandy plains. It is very nearly exclusively carnivorous, feeding on small mammals which it digs up from their burrows. There is a still smaller species with a much darker coat to be found in California. The distribution of the American badgers ranges from latitude 58° in the north to Mexico (Seton, 1910).

The fifth genus, *Helictus*, includes the Ferret-badgers of which there are five Asiatic species. They are terrestrial and burrowing and have long bushy tails. Some are very brightly coloured, such as *H. subaurantiaca*, which is black and orange. The ears are small, the nose grooved, and the palms naked, though the soles of the feet are hairy. Members of this genus are to be found in the Himalayas, Central China, Burma, Borneo, and Formosa.

The last genus, *Melogale*, is also Asiatic, and is closely related to the last in general characters. In fact, Pocock considers the genus to be synonymous with *Helictus*, but Simpson (1945) considers it to be a good genus.

The European badger, *Meles meles* Linnaeus, is very widely distributed in Europe and Asia, and it is not surprising that it shows some variation. The following subspecies have been named:

TYPE: *Meles meles meles* Linnaeus 1758. Generally distributed in Europe and Asia.

Meles meles leptorhynchus Milne-Edwards 1867. Reported from E. Europe, N. Asia, Russian Turkestan, and N. China.

Meles meles arenarius Satunin 1895. From the plains north of the Caspian.

Meles meles minor Satunin 1905. From Transcaucasia.

Meles meles rhodius Festa 1914. From the Island of Rhodes.

Meles meles ponticus Blackler 1916. From N. E. Asia Minor.

Meles meles caucasicus Ognev 1926. From the Caucasus.

Meles meles tauricus Ognev 1926. From the Crimea.

Meles meles hepneri Ognev 1931. From N. E. Caucasus and the plains north of the Caucasus.

For many of these there is not really enough material and data available at the moment to say whether their rank of subspecies is fully justified. I am indebted to the British Museum authorities for the information about the subspecies quoted above.

The genus *Meles* is a fairly old one, bones having many times been discovered in juxtaposition with those of animals long since extinct, such as the Cave-Bear. It is still doubtful how far back the genus goes, as some of the evidence is not conclusive, but A. T. Hopwood writes: 'The genus is first recorded from the Lower Pliocene of Asia and the Upper Pliocene of Europe, but there is some doubt whether the identification is correct. Badgers in the modern sense have not yet been found in British deposits earlier than the Middle Pleistocene (i.e. approximately 250,000 years ago).'

The badger is found practically all over Europe where the country is hilly and wooded. It is absent from the northernmost part of Scandinavia and from N. Russia. You find it in the Iberian Peninsula and in Italy on the one hand, and in the wooded valleys of Norway and Sweden on the other. It is common in Germany, though not so common as formerly. This applies especially to the Black Forest and the wooded hills of South Germany. In France it is widely distributed, but probably only really common in the Vosges Mountains.

It occurs fairly commonly in the Balkans, and is also reported from some of the islands of the Mediterranean including Crete and Rhodes.

In Asia it is not found much north of a line from where the River Tobol meets the River Ob to the north of Amurland. Thus in West Asia badgers are to be found near the Arctic Circle, but in the East the northern limit is much farther south. No doubt this is due to the mountain masses of North-East Asia, which make conditions more severe.

Badgers are to be found in Japan and in most parts of China as far south as the latitude of Hong Kong, with the exception of the higher mountainous parts of West China. The animal's southern limit is defined by the Himalayas, but it is not uncommon in Persia, and has been found at an altitude of 7,000 feet in that country. It is common in Asia Minor.

In Great Britain and Ireland the badger is well distributed and in parts numerous. In fact, it is probably true that there are badgers in every mainland county, Middlesex being a possible exception. It is true that there are parts of England and Scotland where they are decidedly rare, but badgers are easily overlooked and their numbers usually underestimated.

In the Peninsula counties of Cornwall and Devon the badger is very common. In Cornwall it is said that 'there are few parishes in which it may not be found' (Clark, 1906). J. C. Tregarthen (1931) has discussed the distribution of the badger in Cornwall as follows: 'In this wild region, amidst cromlech and stone circle you find the paths beaten by badgers in their goings to and fro, and if you follow you will come on their earths in brake or cairn or other wild surroundings. Another refuge even more favoured than the moor is the belt of cliffs encircling the promontory. The coastline is sparsely dotted with their earths. From St Ives to Land's End there are fourteen sets, from Land's End to Lamorna, twelve; twenty-six in all, averaging one to every mile or so of the coast. These earths have long been in use. Carew, writing of them in 1600, speaks of them as the badger's ancient inheritance. Inland there are eighty-one earths, and of these fifty-seven are distributed amongst the nine westernmost parishes over an area

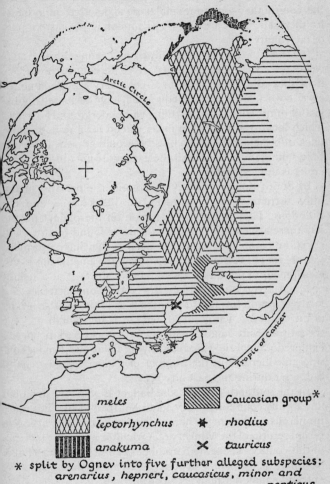

Arctic Circle

Tropic of Cancer

	meles		Caucasian group*
	leptorhynchus	✱	rhodius
	anakuma	✕	tauricus

* split by Ognev into five further alleged subspecies:
arenarius, hepneri, caucasicus, minor and
ponticus.

World distribution of *Meles meles* and its subspecies, and *Meles anakuma* of eighty square miles to the north and west of Penzance.' In this county they sometimes make use of deserted mine-shafts for their sets. They are also very common in the eastern part of the county.

In Devon too they are very numerous. Dening White (1903) writes that ' In the easternmost parts of the county the badger flourishes amazingly. Here on almost every hillside, if not in every covert, are heads of earths which have been used doubt-less for hundreds of years, forming vast underground fortresses which local tradition often avers extend for a mile or more back into the depths of the hills.' It would appear, however, that, taking the county as a whole, they are not quite so numerous as in Cornwall.

In South Somerset they are common, especially in the hilly districts of the Quantocks, the Blackdowns, and the Brendons. They are not so common on the plain, and the sets there are mainly smaller and to be found in the small copses and even hedgerows. On the hills they have enormous sets of great age. Some of these follow the line of the north escarpment of the Blackdowns and are situated at a height of about seven hundred feet. In North Somerset they are fairly common but not so numerous as in the southern part of the county. Their great stronghold is the Mendips. Very recently ancient bones of badgers were discovered in a newly explored part of the Cheddar caves. There has been a con-siderable increase in the number of badgers in this part of Somerset during the past fifty years.

In the southern counties the badger is widely distributed and locally common or very common. In Wiltshire it is more numerous in the north than in the south, but, according to recent returns of the Ministry of Agriculture, is on the increase in this county. There are a number of large sets in the chalky downlands, the white deposits of clean chalk outside the entrances making them very conspicuous.

In Dorset badgers are fairly common, especially in the coastal belt and towards the centre of the county. In the New Forest area of Hampshire they are very numerous, and some of the sets are extremely large. Mortimer Batten tells how the badgers in this region use the drainage gutters that border the rides instead of making their own paths. In North Hampshire they are locally common, but not nearly so numerous as in the south.

Badgers are to be found locally in Sussex and, in a few favoured localities, commonly. W. C. J. Ruskin Butterworth (1905) states that 'In West Sussex it continues to hold its own in nearly all the heavily-wooded districts.' It is not uncommon in East Sussex. During the Second World War the numbers have been reported to be on the increase by the Pest Control Officer for the county.

Badgers are found locally in all the Thames counties. They were described as rare in Kent (Baker, 1908), but that is not a true picture of the position today, when they are locally not uncommon. Towards London they get much rarer, but it is surprising how a few cling on to their old heritage with great tenacity and hardly a soul knows of their existence.

J. A. Bucknill (1902) wrote that 'In Surrey the species is now confined to the most rural districts, but it is only within the last twenty years that it has come to be regarded as at all uncommon. It was once common near Boxhill.' Today the position is much the same, and, although the numbers are greater than is generally realized, they are not by any means common. They still breed regularly in Richmond Park, and old badgers from this preserve occasionally astonish people by roaming beyond the confines of the Park. One was seen at Kew very recently. There are other occupied sets within a radius of ten miles from Charing Cross, but the less said about these the better. Good luck to the badgers there!

In Essex badgers became very scarce towards the end of the last century, but were probably never extinct. More recently they have been reintroduced on several occasions and their numbers have increased at a considerable rate. G. Dent (1922) wrote, 'In S. E. Essex they are especially numerous about Laindon, Grays, Tilbury, Dawes Heath, and the surrounding country. On one farm of a thousand acres I dug out twelve full-grown badgers in 1920.' They are also common in the

Epping Forest region, but in the north of the county they are much less common.

They occur locally in the more hilly districts of Hertfordshire, where some large sets are to be found. They are widely distributed but nowhere very common in this county. In Berkshire too they are not uncommon at the present time in the well-wooded districts. In Oxfordshire, Charles Elton (1929) wrote, 'They are well distributed and by no means rare. They are probably most common in the north half of the county. The burrows are nearly always in woods. Reports during the past few years suggest that their numbers are increasing and that now the population may be described as heavy.' In Buckinghamshire they are still fairly represented on the large estates, and even in the more open country their sets are to be found.

In the flat lands of East Anglia they are decidedly rarer. Records during the early years of this century are few and far between, only odd ones being reported from Norfolk and Cambridge. Recently their numbers have increased and they are not uncommon near the Bedfordshire border. But this is not badger country, the habitat is the reverse of typical, and badgers breeding there may be looked upon as immigrants from the more hilly districts of the west. Thus they become commoner in Bedfordshire and Huntingdonshire, and in Northamptonshire they are widespread and locally common.

In the Severn counties badgers are common and in parts numerous. In the Cotswold country of Gloucestershire they are very common and many of the sets are large. Names such as Brockworth and Brockhampton tell of the prevalence of badgers in more remote times. In West Gloucestershire they are not so common, but they are nevertheless widespread.

The numbers in Monmouth and Hereford (Lindsay, 1908) are large, and they are frequent in Worcestershire, where they are said to be on the increase according to recent Ministry of Agriculture returns; there are some ancient strongholds in the Malverns.

In Warwickshire R. F. Tams (1904) described them as rare, but more recently Arthur R. Thompson (1931), who studied the animal intensively, stated that they were common in parts. During the past five years they have been described as numerous and increasing by the Pest Control Officer for the county.

In Staffordshire they are also common locally and are reported to be on the increase. Millais (1904) describes one set in this county where forty-four holes were visible at one and the same time. 'A. E.' (1903) mentioned a most interesting case of a litter of badger cubs being found above ground. To quote his own words, 'he found a litter of five badgers lying in a shallow nest with no protection beyond that afforded by gorse bushes.' He added that there were plenty of strong earths in the neighbourhood much used by badgers.

In Shropshire they are common. Frances Pitt (1935) has shown that during the last forty years the badger population has increased considerably in the wheatland district of the county.

In Lincolnshire, at the end of the last century, Sir Alfred Pease (1895) described them as being present in small numbers. Today they are probably absent from the Holland district, but are increasing in Kesteven and Lindsey. In a recent letter to the *Gamekeeper and Countryside*, 'Enquirer' (March, 1947) stated that badgers had recently become quite numerous near Louth.

In Leicestershire and Rutland they are fairly frequently met with. Eric Hardy (1944) mentioned how he saw 'a badger grunting its way along an allotment garden on the edge of Leicester' in daylight. In Nottinghamshire a similar state of affairs exists, and the density of badgers may be described as light to medium. In Derbyshire they are frequently met with in the hilly districts, and recently they have been reported to be on the increase.

Cheshire also has many badger localities. A.W. Boyd wrote to me (1947) that the badger is widely distributed in the county. In the Northwich region it is not found in great numbers, but there are many sets scattered over that area. In the Delamere Forest region, however, they are common. They have also been reported from Wirral by Hardy (1944).

Two hundred years ago badgers were common in Lancashire. They are now rather uncommon but hardly rare. Eric Hardy (1944) writes that they occur along the Ribble valley, and near Southport. Also that they are to be found in the Cotterill's Clough Nature Sanctuary on the outskirts of Manchester.

In the Lake District today the badger position is very different from what it was in 1900, when badgers were said to be nearly extinct (Macpherson, 1901). Richard Clapham, writing to me recently, said that 'There are plenty of badgers in Cumberland and Westmorland. A certain number live on the Westmorland Fells, but they are found mainly in the low ground and amongst the big woods such as those on both sides of Lake Windermere.' Ritson Graham (1946) gives a most excellent account of the badger's distribution in Cumberland. He writes, 'Though the present distribution of the badger is fairly general throughout the county, it is nevertheless patchy; there are parts of comparative density and others of relative scarcity.' He continues, 'There is no evidence of mountain-top dwelling by the badgers of either the central fells or the Pennines. The hard and elevated core of central Lakeland is now, however, in process of being penetrated ... The badger is undoubtedly climbing back to the mountain strongholds of its ancestors.' Ritson Graham mentions many districts where badger haunts are plentiful, including the valleys of the rivers Lyne, King, Irthing, and Cambeck in North Cumberland; the valleys of the rivers Gelt, Croglin, and Raven in the Pennine region, and also the main valley of the river Eden. 'In the Cumberland plain,' he continues, 'the streamsides are again the chief haunts, yet there are many earths established away from the narrow and often wooded valleys. The limestone country about Greystoke and the red earth around Penrith contain many badger strongholds. ... In the Solway region the badger is established in all but the actual coastal strip, and its extension in this direction is of comparatively recent origin. ... Inland from the industrial belt of W. Cumberland, the wooded and stream-intersected zone between the central region and the sea is fairly well occupied by the badgers. There are many earths in a wide district round Cockermouth, including the Lorton and Derwent valleys. In all these districts there is a sprinkling of very old, and maybe ancient, badger sets, as well as a few traditional haunts not now occupied. The majority, however, in all localities, are of fairly recent origin, the outcome of the last twenty-five years of increase in the species, an increase which continues, though perhaps during the recent years, less rapidly than hitherto.'

The badger is absent from the Isle of Man.

In Yorkshire badgers are found all over the county and are common in parts. They occur commonly in the hilly districts between Scarborough and York, and the region north-east of Scarborough. In the Pennine valleys they are also quite plentiful. Taking the county as a whole, it may be said that they are very widespread.

In Northumberland and Durham forty years ago they were present in small numbers, and this is still true of the former county, but in Durham there has been a marked increase in recent years. Ministry of Agriculture reports go so far as to say that the population may now be regarded as heavy (1946).

The badger is to be found all over Wales, and in places commonly. Only in Caernarvon is it scarce. Professor Brambell, writing to me of the badger in this county, said that, although he knew of localities, they were scarce generally and very local. This has not always been the case, as H. E. Forrest (1907) wrote: 'They are not uncommon, especially along the north and east borders.' He went on, 'They are not indigenous in Anglesey, but there is now one earth at Plâs Newydd Park. ... It is supposed that badgers got there originally by crossing over the Menai Bridge by night.'

Badgers are not uncommon in Denbigh and Flint. Gwion Davies (1936) has published figures of the number of sets occupied in the district around Denbigh. Of the twenty he mentions, nineteen were situated between 100 and 650 feet, and one at 900. They are rather scarce in Merioneth, though there is some evidence of a recent increase. In Montgomery they are much more numerous, and this also applies to Radnor.

In South Wales they are widely distributed. Dr Colin

Matheson kindly supplied me with data he had collected which confirmed this. He informed me that they were far from scarce in Glamorgan and that there were quite a few earths in the near neighbourhood of Cardiff. There are many sets in Pembrokeshire, where the Pest Control Officer describes the present population as heavy. They also occur in Carmarthen in some numbers.

In Scotland there are few large areas where there are no badgers, but they are never really common. In the Western Lowlands they are found locally in Wigtown and Ayr; more commonly in Kirkcudbright and Dumfries. In the East Lowlands they are more numerous, being found locally in Peebles but more commonly in the counties adjoining the East coast, e.g. Berwick. Mortimer Batten wrote to me recently that 'You can take it that there is one badger set on every estate throughout E. Lothian certainly.'

In the East Highlands they are widely distributed, and W. Marshall (1935) wrote, 'There are probably more badgers in the Spey Valley area west of Kingussie and around Loch Laggan than any other part of Scotland, but even here they are not numerous.' Mortimer Batten says they are not uncommon in Perthshire.

In the Northern Highlands they are much rarer, but they do exist in Ross and Sutherland, especially in the Dunrobin and Reay Forest areas, and even as far north as Tongue.

They are not numerous in the Western Highlands, but they are widespread. Mortimer Batten (1946) writes, 'In the Loch Awe district they are all over the braes there, just a warren here and there, not so common as the foxes, of course, but nowhere absent.'

They are not native on any of the outer islands, but Harvie-Brown (1882) mentions that the badger was introduced into Jura and upon Ailsa Craig. It did not survive long on Ailsa Craig.

In the more mountainous districts of Scotland badgers are probably more frequent than is generally supposed, as little earth is thrown out from their sets to give their presence away. As Mortimer Batten (1946) remarks, 'Tracks in the snow and

the findings of terriers give most indication of their presence.'
Darling (1947) has recently published an informative map of
the distribution of the badger in the Highlands.

Badgers are to be found in every county of Ireland, and in
some of these they are common. As in England, it is true to
say that they are more frequent in the hilly country and more
common in the west than the east.

They are very well established in the south-western counties
of Kerry and Cork, and in the west they are to be found locally common in Clare, Limerick, Galway, and Mayo. C.B.
Moffatt (1927) states that 'R. M. Barrington made a list of
two hundred and two badgers that to his knowledge had been
killed in thirty out of thirty-two counties of Ireland in the
eight years 1901–8.' This list did not include any from Clare,
which was well known as a stronghold of the species. But it is
not only in the more remote parts of Ireland that they occur.
Moffatt relates how inhabitants of a house, 'well within the
city limits of Dublin in 1926, were startled one April morning
by a badger on their premises.'

It can be seen from this account that the badger in the
British Isles is very widely distributed. It must be realized,
however, that, owing to its nocturnal habits and unobtrusive
ways, it is often overlooked and its numbers grossly underestimated except by those who have studied them intensively.
There are, I think, two important reasons for this wide distribution: the adaptability of badgers as regards food, and the
security afforded them by their sets. Their nocturnal habits
also probably help them to remain unnoticed and therefore
help them to survive. Their omnivorous habits allow them to
exist in most types of country though much more food is available for them all the year round in the south and west. So,
although lack of food does not ban them from any part, it
certainly affects the density of the population.

Altitude also seems to affect considerably the badger's distribution. They are nowhere common where the country is
flat, especially so if the land is liable to be flooded at certain
seasons. This is, I think, undoubtedly the main reason for the
comparative rarity of badgers in East Anglia. In other parts

of the British Isles, where flat country has its badger population, the reason appears to be a regular overflow from the more typical hilly country not far off. Badgers occur most commonly between one hundred and six hundred feet, but

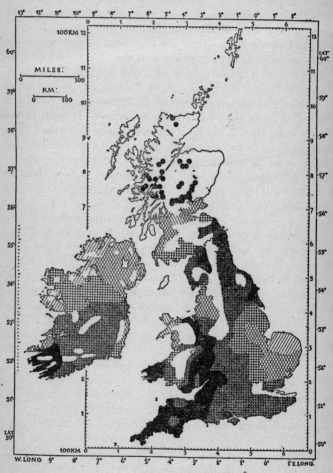

British distribution of *Meles meles* L. (see explanation on opposite page)

they are also to be found much higher up mountain sides, this being more true of Scotland and parts of Wales. Their scarcity at high altitudes, as in the Lake district, is probably influenced by the poorer food supply, and the presence of more suitable localities at lower altitudes near by, rather than the inability to live under these conditions.

The fact that sets are usually near water is probably not very important in Britain as a limiting factor, as in badger country typical from other points of view water is never far off. It cannot, however, be ignored that sets are more often near water than otherwise.

Security from its enemies is greater in some types of country than in others, and this is an important factor. Man is the badger's worst enemy, and in many parts badgers are locally rare owing to man's encroachment and persecution. In rocky country sets are more impregnable and the badger can hold its own without difficulty; and in the less cultivated areas is

---

British distribution of *Meles meles L.* (see map on opposite page)

The distribution of the badger in the Highlands of Scotland follows that shown in F. Fraser Darling (1947) p. 278. In this area each dot represents the intersection of two 10-km. lines of the National Grid nearest to each place believed to be inhabited by the species in the breeding season. In the rest of Britain the distribution of the badger has been divided by the author between areas of six different kinds, chosen by him from his study of the literature and correspondence with observers. It must be stressed that the categories are based on observation and experience, and not on any precise measurement in other than a few small areas. The map will certainly have to be revised as a result of future studies. The densest areas, shown black, represent areas with a relatively high proportion of woodland and scrub in which badgers are known to be abundant, the extent of their abundance having been particularly remarked upon in the literature. The quadruple-hatched area represents that in which badgers are known to be common and to be found in every suitable covert. The areas double-hatched vertically and horizontally are those in which the badger is relatively rare. In those areas with double diagonal hatching the badger is a member of the fauna but decidedly local and patchy in its distribution. The areas single-hatched diagonally represent those in which the badger is extremely scarce and apparently on the verge of extinction. From white areas the badger appears to be totally absent: most of these are built-up or mountain-top areas.

commoner, since there is less interference. In some parts of Scotland, however, badgers are much rarer than they were, owing to the persistent attention of gamekeepers on the game moors, but the opposite is also true; on estates where they have been afforded protection they are easily holding their own. In my own opinion man is the most important limiting factor as far as numbers and distribution are concerned for most parts of England. Systematic persecution might easily reduce the badgers' numbers very greatly, and in some counties bring about their extinction, but in the wilder parts, where badgers have defied their enemies for many thousands of years, it is unlikely that their numbers would be reduced to danger point. With a saner human attitude towards animal life generally and a greater realization of the usefulness of the badger, its future should be assured in most parts of rural Britain.

CHAPTER 4

GETTING TO KNOW THE ANIMALS

BADGERS are capable of travelling long distances in a night, but it would appear that if food is plentiful they will remain within a mile or so of their sets during most of the year. This does not apply to unmated animals, especially males during the breeding season.

The area which was studied most intensively had the advantage of being a somewhat isolated patch of woodland covering some forty-five acres. It was considered likely that this area was able to support a badger population quite comfortably without the necessity for its members to wander far to find food. By taking regular counts of these badgers (if that could be done), it was thought that their movements could be accurately determined without having to allow for strangers from neighbouring sets except at the breeding season; and any sudden reduction in numbers which was permanent would represent the time when any left the district.

This woodland area was known as Conigre Wood, and it is part of the Rendcomb Park estate. It was situated in a part of the Cotswolds where badgers are plentiful. The first thing to be done was to map out the area and mark on it any features that seemed to be significant from the point of view of the badgers. It was found that in 1943 there were five sets in the wood which were in temporary or permanent use by the badgers. Of these, two were large and well established, two were smaller but regularly used, and the fifth was represented only by a single hole and was only occasionally inhabited.

Towards the end of the summer the tracks leading from the various sets became very plain, and a map was made of these paths to show how they connected up. Several interesting facts came to light as a result of this mapping. Being creatures of habit, using the same routes time and time again, it followed that the more definite the path the more important it was to the badgers during their everyday existence. By following these paths it became possible to discover why these particular ones were used so much. The ones most used were those which led from one set to another, suggesting that badgers were to some extent social, and that families did not necessarily live as independent units but paid each other visits constantly. Alternatively, it might have been argued that all the badgers lived together but constantly changed their quarters.

Some of the paths were comparatively straight and led down the slope of the wood for a considerable distance. These were so obvious that they looked artificial, and, in fact, people did use them as footpaths, but they were, beyond doubt, primarily badger tracks, as occasionally they led under a fallen tree or low branches. Here people would make a detour to avoid the obstruction, but the badger path continued right under it. These particular paths could be traced for some five hundred yards; and they led to the river Churn which flowed along the valley at the foot of the wood. Badgers usually make their sets within reasonable distance of a river, and it was assumed that these paths were made when journeying to and from their drinking places.

By carefully examining the river bank, badger dung was found in pits dug near a fir copse, and there appeared to be a path leading to the river at that point. Sand was put down here, wetted and smoothed, and the next morning badger footmarks showed up plainly. It was now established that this was one of their drinking places.

Some parts of the wood were littered with stones flaked off from the limestone, and special paths led to these. At night the badgers were often heard here, turning the stones with a clatter or shoving them aside with their paws. It is probable that they searched here for ground beetles and slugs, as every now and then an excited yelp would tell of the discovery of some delicacy.

Other parts of the wood were overgrown with rosebay willow herb, and tracks were very numerous here. At one place all the rosebay was beaten flat over an area of about forty square yards. This was one of their playgrounds, where the badgers would stop for a little while in the summer after leaving their sets until the essential task of feeding drew them away. Here they would chase each other like puppies, tumbling head over heels in their excitement. From this playground paths radiated out in all directions.

One curious spot was a large bramble bush which had been hollowed out inside. Several paths led to it, and its floor was covered with a quantity of dry moss brought from some distance. I believe this was a sleeping-out place. I was never able to prove it as it was impossible to approach it without noise, with all the rosebay around, but I know of no other likely explanation. I have read how on one occasion it was possible to creep up to one of these sleeping-out places and two badgers were seen fast asleep. This bush in Conigre was an ideal spot for the purpose as a badger could get away in any direction very quickly if danger approached.

A large area of the wood was an ash association with a ground flora of bluebells and dog's mercury as co-dominants. There were many plants here with succulent underground storage organs, and these provided food of a different kind for the badgers. Here you could see where roots had been dug up and eaten.

Several paths led right out of the wood on to pasture land and scrub. They soon became indistinguishable, but their general direction suggested what the animals used them for. They were probably used on wet nights when earthworms were lying in abundance on the damp turf, and when beetles were to be found under the dung.

The map on p. 52 shows the relationship between the various sets and paths. For convenience the five sets are labelled as letters of the alphabet. A and C are the largest, B and D are smaller, while E is only of minor importance.

Having mapped out the area, the next step was to get to know the animals inhabiting it. How many badgers were here, spread out among the various sets in the wood? Several methods of counting them were tried. The obvious and *apparently* most accurate method was to watch at a set and count any badgers seen. This was found however to give most unreliable results. On one occasion a set would be watched and perhaps four badgers seen; a night or so later there would be none in residence. Others might be heard in different parts

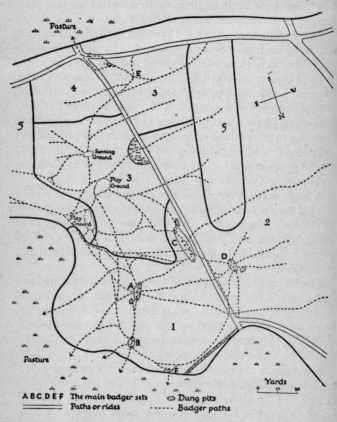

ABC DEF The main badger sets   ⬭ Dung pits
━━━━━ Paths or rides   - - - - - Badger paths

Map of part of Conigre Wood to show badger community in relation to dominant vegetation.

Area 1. Mixed woodland with ground flora, mainly dog's mercury. Area 2. Ash trees dominant, with a varied and flourishing ground flora of bluebells, dog's mercury, wood-anemones, etc. Area 3. Black poplars planted sparsely. Ground flora of rosebay willow-herb. Area 4. Birches and poplars with more rosebay. Area 5. Beech dominant. Ground flora almost nil.

of the wood, suggesting that they had moved off to another set in the area. In fact it was extremely difficult to forecast where they would be at any one time.

Other observers had used the method of placing sticks across the mouths of the sets and noting the next day if they had been moved. Gwion Davies for example states that 'the presence of a fox or badger can be tested by placing two upright sticks in the mouth of a set ... the sticks will be pushed aside if a badger comes out.' In this way working around Denbigh he determined which sets were in use. This method was therefore tried, but the results were both unreliable and misleading and it was found that the conclusions to be drawn from such experiments must be modified by other considerations. For instance the sticks could be knocked over by animals other than badgers. Very often the sets were inhabited by other species including foxes and rabbits. It is true that if the sticks were carefully placed it was possible for a rabbit to emerge without touching them while a fox or badger would have to push them aside, but foxes may be as common as badgers or more so. This is not insurmountable as the fox leaves a scent sufficient even for the novice to recognize his presence in a set. But there are other more serious difficulties. The sticks can be moved if a badger goes in as well as when it comes out, and the final position of the sticks is often no indication of which way the animal was going. My faith in this method for regular counts was finally shattered while watching at C after I had put sticks across each of the five main entrances. While I watched, a badger came trotting towards me from another set; it paused at the first entrance, putting its snout down the hole to sniff and find out, presumably, if other badgers were there; in doing so it pushed the sticks aside. Smelling none of its friends, it went to the next and repeated the process, finally disappearing up the ride, leaving four out of five entrances with no sticks! I waited on but no badgers emerged.

On many other occasions I have found that during the summer it is the usual practice of badgers to pay visits to their neighbours before going off to feed, and so, at this season at any rate, the stick method is unreliable. It is, however, possible to get some indication of distribution by this method if the technique is modified and if other evidence is taken into account by way of confirmation. I have found, for instance, that if sticks were put across all holes in the wood, and then one set watched, it was possible, after counting them at this set visually, to go quickly round to the others and observe the sticks before the badgers had time to visit each other. There is time for this because it is the usual practice for them to have a period of play before they leave the vicinity of their sets.

After badgers have taken up their winter quarters they seldom move their abode unless they have been badly frightened – such as when all entrances have been blocked by a Hunt. At this season they are mainly paired if adult, and they visit each other far less: I consider that at this time of year the stick method is fairly reliable.

Another way of discovering whether a set is occupied is to note if any fresh dung is deposited near by. Usually pits are dug within twenty yards of the set (though there are notable exceptions), and by watching these you have a good indication of their presence. This is usually reliable, but on several occasions it has proved wrong in my experience. I was watching badgers one morning in August before dawn, and when daylight came they went underground. On going the round, I found fresh dung near one set, and decided to try for a photograph that evening, assuming that it was inhabited. That night no badger emerged, and a full count was registered from other sets. This occurred at set D, and I have since found that badgers at C often use the pits dug near D when the latter is unoccupied.

It can thus be seen that none of these methods by itself was capable of giving reliable results. The visual one was the best for single sets; but it was not possible to watch all the sets at the same time. This was remedied by getting a willing band of helpers, each set being watched by one person: when all the badgers that came out were counted the total was reliable. Although I am convinced that this was quite the best

54

method, it was not every time that full counts were made. The human factor was multiplied five times, and there was a greater chance that one person should be discovered by a badger before the others emerged and the resulting fright prevent the rest from coming out. However, one thing was certain: the minimum number at any rate was obtained each time; and by repeating the count on several occasions the full number soon became evident.

By this method it was established that there were nine badgers in Conigre Wood during the summer of 1943, nine in 1944, and eleven in 1945. The significance of these numbers will be discussed later.

Some thirty years ago it was generally considered that the badger was a rare animal. Whether this was actually the case is difficult to assess, but it seems to be quite definite that since that time the species has been on the increase in this country. Frances Pitt made a survey of the wheatland country of Shropshire and found thirty-seven occupied sets in an area comprising eighty-five square miles. From this she calculated that about one hundred animals occupied the area. This estimate was based on the amount of winter usage shown by the holes. When the set showed a good deal of traffic in mid-winter with footprints differing in size, she assumed at least two badgers were present. When the set was very big and the usage still more pronounced, two couples were assumed to be there. She also made enquiries as to how many sets were present in the same district in 1900, thirty-four years before, and only ten could be accounted for with a population of possibly twenty-four animals.

The same sort of thing seems to have occurred in the Cotswolds. In Conigre Wood, one set (C) goes back beyond living memory, but thirty years ago it was the only set in the wood. Soon after the First World War, the site at A was a rabbit warren, and it was not until 1924 that it was established as an offshoot from C. Trapping in the district occurred regularly on a small scale to keep the animals down, and no further increase was noted until 1938, when B was opened up as an offshoot from A. B was at first a single hole and only used periodically, but after foxes had used it for a litter of four cubs in 1939 it was used for breeding purposes by badgers the following year. It has been enlarged and used regularly since. In 1939, D was dug out by badgers. Previously this was a rabbit warren, then it was taken over by a vixen which had cubs there, and in the summer of 1939 was greatly enlarged by badgers, two other entrances being pushed out. It has not, however, been used for badger cubs to date, but only as temporary quarters. On two occasions it has been used in the autumn by a mated pair, but on both occasions they moved off to larger and safer quarters when winter set in. E is a small set with only a single entrance; it has never been used for breeding purposes. It was dug out in 1943, and used on odd days by single badgers only. It might be described as the spare bedroom of the community.

A set may be described as established when a breeding pair has used it, and there seems to be a general plan of development. In Conigre, for example, there was the main set with its mated pair at C. Then A was dug out as an outlier for purposes of change from C. This later became enlarged and was used during the winter by a mated pair; and there were cubs in the spring. After some years outliers from both A and C were formed at B and D respectively, and today one of these (B) is used regularly for breeding purposes, but the other is not yet so. Can this development go on indefinitely? There is some evidence that Conigre Wood now has a maximum population of mated pairs; if this number is exceeded there may not be enough food for all during the critical period when cubs are small and unable to travel far. That this saturation point has been reached is suggested by the facts that three pairs have used the sets for three consecutive years, and that a new set was established in a strip of woodland about a mile across the valley. No badgers had previously been there, and this set's formation in September 1945 coincided with a drop in numbers in Conigre.

There is a good deal of other evidence from this neighbourhood that the sets are more numerous than formerly, and that since 1914 a good many new sets have been established. I

56

believe that this increase is true for most parts of the country. Frances Pitt (1935) has gone into the question in some detail, and she is convinced of the increase. She bases her conclusions on facts obtained 'from naturalist correspondents, sporting friends and gamekeepers, from comments in sporting journals, and from the annual returns made by Masters of Hounds to the journal *Horse and Hound* in which they give their "bags". Badgers now figure largely in these returns which are made by practically all packs.'

Reading through the various County Histories, most of which were written in the early nineteen hundreds, I have been struck by the different estimates given of badger frequency compared with those of today. This applies specially to the home counties, but it is not limited to these by any means.

Some evidence from the Bristol area is given by H. E. Tetley (1940): 'Evidently a great change in its favour has come over the badger since the last two reports. Described in the *Brit. Ass. Handbook to Bristol Neighbourhood*, 1898, p. 202, "The badger which used to be common is still a member of the fauna in our district", and by Rudge and Charbonnier, 1909, p. 58, "Maintains its numbers in a few places but it has disappeared from many of its old haunts", the badger can now be said to be common in both parts of the Bristol district. It is to be found in many places on the higher ground, from about two hundred feet upwards, where conditions are suitable for it.'

The badger was said to be extinct in the Lake District towards the end of the last century. Dickinson (1875) stated that 'Badgers are now extinct in the wild state in Cumberland but were not scarce until about the end of the eighteenth century.' It is probable, however, that the point of extinction was never quite reached. Macpherson (1901) states, 'Formerly badger earths were to be found in most parts of the country, from the shores of Solway Firth to the borders of Westmorland. Some years ago it appeared probable that the old race of badgers had become extinct, but of late years badgers have reasserted their rights of domicile in some of our larger covers. Whether these animals had escaped from confinement is difficult to determine, but as wild badgers certainly exist in Westmorland, it is possible that though the number of badgers in Cumberland dwindled to very small proportions the original stock never became entirely extinct.'

Ritson Graham (1946) has studied the increase of the badger in Cumberland and its distribution, and he has kindly allowed me to quote from his excellent account. He leaves no doubt that the increase in numbers has been very marked, and writing of the period following the First World War he says, ' I find my first year's list of earths visited rose from seven to twenty-seven, and that two years later the number had increased to fifty-two. Though the increase has been less remarkable during the succeeding year it has nevertheless continued, and new haunts continually come to my notice at a greater rate than my limited time allows for their inspection.'

In my own part of Somerset the density of the population is difficult to assess with accuracy, but in the immediate neighbourhood of Rendcomb I know of fifteen sets in an area of about eighteen square miles. The larger sets certainly have a normal population of three mated pairs, though trapping is extensive and the numbers fluctuate as a result. Cubs, in my opinion, soon take the place of trapped animals, and tend to keep the numbers up to saturation point for that particular set or locality – hence the exasperation of a local landlord who traps badgers regularly on his estate, but never succeeds in reducing the numbers for more than one season although he has caught as many as six in a season from one set. There are probably about twenty-eight pairs regularly inhabiting fifteen sets mentioned above, which gives a density of roughly three badgers per square mile.

Badgers have few enemies, man undoubtedly being the chief. It is strange that man should persecute them so much in spite of the indisputable fact that they do much more good than harm. Partly, no doubt, it is due to ignorance, partly because badgers' skins have a small marketable value, and

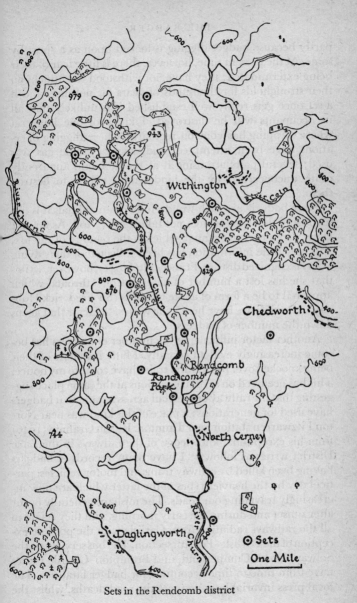

Withington

River Coln

River Churn

Chedworth

Rendcomb

Rendcomb Park

North Cerney

River Churn

Daglingworth

⊙ Sets

One Mile

Sets in the Rendcomb district

partly because badger-digging is looked upon as a sport by some. At the present time, however, there is little fear of their being exterminated; they have not withstood the attacks on their strongholds for thousands of years for nothing, and if a set once gets really well established it is unlikely that all its occupants will be destroyed. I know of one large set where trapping has gone on regularly, where digging operations have been attempted, and where cyanide gas was used; several pairs are using it at the moment, apparently quite unconcerned by the landowner's efforts to destroy them.

Since badgers are such wonderfully clean animals it is not surprising that disease does not take a heavy toll. As far as I know they never get mange which is the scourge of the fox, and very little information has been collected of their dying of any recognized disease. Frances Pitt (1941), however, writes that she has lost a number of badgers from 'throats' which appeared to be a form of acute tonsilitis (Sir Frederick Hobday). 'Possibly we have here', she writes, 'a factor that keeps down the number of badgers.'

Another factor influencing the number of badgers has become increasingly evident recently. Many instances of their being knocked over by cars and trains have come to my notice. This has occurred on several occasions at the same place suggesting that the railway or road cut across a route that badgers have used for generations; a place of this kind was near Norton Fitzwarren station near Taunton. Ritson Graham (1946) from his exceptional knowledge of the railways in the Lake District writes as follows: 'I have many records of badgers having been killed by railway trains and motor vehicles, particularly by the heavier types of the latter which are now increasingly travelling our roads. The mishaps generally occur after sunset and during the early morning, and they relate to all the railways radiating from Carlisle with the possible exception of the Carlisle–Penrith section. The bus services on the Solway, North Cumberland, and Brampton–Carlisle routes have from time to time accounted for badger fatalities. The local press invariably announces the road deaths, whilst the drivers of the railway locomotives concerned usually report such instances to me.'

I have also read of several instances of badgers being electrocuted on railway lines. I have the impression that these accidents are more common than is generally realized. It is surprising for example how many people, who have only seen a badger once or twice, have seen them on these occasions in the light of their headlamps, or dead beside the road.

It is a mystery where badgers go to die. I have a theory that they die in one of their underground chambers which is then walled in by the others. Later generations when tunnelling come upon the skeletons and eventually push out the bones with the bedding and earth at the set entrance. Several times I have picked up badger skulls and other bones from the debris outside a set, and this is the only explanation I can think of. I have only found the bones outside well-established sets. Ritson Graham (1946) also comments upon badgers' bones being found in a similar way.

It would appear however that on certain occasions at any rate badgers will bury their dead in specially excavated holes away from the set in which they have been living. Brian Vesey-FitzGerald (1942) gave an amazing account of how in June he witnessed a badger's funeral. In this instance the sow had lost her mate. She came to the set entrance and let out a weird unearthly cry; then she departed for a rabbit warren not far distant. There she excavated a large hole in preparation for the body of her mate. She worked at this over a long period, the time being broken up at intervals by journeyings between warren and set. After some hours a second badger appeared, a male. The sow stood still with nose lowered to the ground and back ruffling agitatedly, and the male slowly approached with nose also lowered. Then the female, moving her head swiftly up and down, uttered a whistling sound 'as though the wind had been sharply expelled through the nostrils'; at the same time she moved forward with two tiny jerky steps. When she stopped the male went through a similar motion, his nose to the ground like the sow's. This was repeated. The ritual over, they both retired down the set. After some time they reappeared, the male dragging the dead badger by a hind leg and the sow somehow helping from behind. They reached the warren, interred the body, and covered it with earth. Then the male departed and the sow returned to her set and disappeared. One wonders if all badgers are buried in this way or whether these rites are characteristic only of such special occasions as when a sow loses her mate.

CHAPTER 5

THE FOOD OF BADGERS

MAN is always quick to notice any animal habit that has a harmful effect on his own property or interests. The good habits are often overlooked and the bad ones over-emphasized in consequence. The badger for hundreds of years has been a persecuted animal, and misconceptions regarding the food that it eats provide one of the reasons for this persecution.

The badger is a member of the order Carnivora and has large canine teeth. You would expect it to be a flesh-eater; but although this is true in part it is by no means the whole story. At certain times of the year there is less animal matter in the badger's diet than vegetable. There are not many omnivorous animals, but the badger is certainly one of them. It is for this reason that so many conflicting statements have been made regarding its food.

It is not easy to be certain what a nocturnal animal feeds on, especially one as shy as a badger, and many statements are obviously incorrect because only circumstantial evidence was obtained. There are a number of methods which can be employed to find out what a mammal feeds on, and I have used most of these in the case of the badger. Three of these methods can be relied upon to be completely accurate.

The first is to examine the stomach contents of the animals that have been killed. I had no intention of killing large numbers of badgers for this purpose, so I was only able to examine the limited number of dead badgers that came my way. This method, although excellent in theory, is subject to great difficulty because the badger, being nocturnal, is not usually dug out or knocked over by a car when its stomach is full. In badger-digging the animal is usually killed in the afternoon, and when knocked over by a car it is as a rule during the early part of the night before it has had a chance to feed much.

By this time the stomach is practically empty. However, I have been able to analyse a few successfully and I can quote two other cases. Many more, however, will have to be examined before a complete picture is obtained.

The details of those examined are as follows:

(1) 16 March 1944. Rendcomb, Glos. E.G.N.

Much of the material was digested, but the following were identified:

Fur of young rabbit.
Pieces of small rabbit bones.
Numerous earthworms nearly digested but recognizable by the gizzard and spermathecae.
Larva of a large ground beetle.
Numerous small slugs.
Much vegetable material, at this stage of digestion about three parts vegetable to one part animal. It included the following:
Grass.
Roots.
Underground storage organs, probably rhizomes.
New shoots of dog's mercury.
A large roll of sycamore bark.

(2) 25 May 1947. Wiveliscombe, Somerset. E.G.N.

Digestion far advanced but the following identified:

Much rabbit fur, average length of hairs ½ inch.
High proportion of grass.
An ash fruit.
A few unidentified seeds.

(3) 7 June 1947. Wiveliscombe, Somerset.

The various remains of two young rabbits, including fur and bones in large fragments. Soft parts already digested.
Remains of several beetles (*Geotrupes* sp.).
Grass in small quantity.

(4) 29 September 1946. Near Taunton, Somerset. E.G.N.

Most material digested, but the following identified:

Beetles of the genus *Geotrupes*, at least twenty.

Earthworms, at least ten.
Fur of young rabbit.
Tooth of young rabbit.
Four lepidopterous larvae (Noctuids).
Two ground-beetles.
Larva of large Staphylinid beetle, probably *Staphylinus olens*.
Several small slugs.
Acorns, a very large number broken up into fairly large pieces.
Grass, in some quantity.
A clover leaf.
Various small leaves.

The proportion of plant to animal matter at this stage of digestion was about three to one by volume.

(5) 4 October 1947. Near Langport, Somerset.

Stomach was nearly empty, but contained a plum stone, a number of beetle remains and some material too far digested to be recognized. The colon and rectum were, however, full, and the following were identified:

Forty-five large beetles of the genus *Geotrupes*, the number estimated by counting the elytra.
Two pear stalks and pieces of skin. Also ten pips presumably from the same.
A number of beech nuts.
A little grass, but probably incidental judging by the small amount present.
Much material unrecognizable.

(6) 6 November 1945. Near Rendcomb, Glos. E.G.N.

Digestion well advanced.

A very large number of earthworms.
Several small slugs.
A great mass of unrecognizable fibrous plant material including:
Leaves.
Roots.
Grass.

N.B. The night before was very wet.

(7) 1 December 1945. Rendcomb, Glos. E. G. N.

Digestion almost completed, and very little recognizable except a lot of fibrous vegetable matter.

(8) 17 July 1935. Bagley Wood, Near Oxford. A. D. Middleton.

Four hedgehogs. All appeared to be adults. Only three spines swallowed.
Four young rabbits from the nest, three or four days old and decapitated.
Four other young mammals from a nest. These were much mangled and may have been young water-voles or moles.
Numerous bee cocoons with bees and larvae.
One ground-beetle, genus *Carabus*.

(9) Early September 1946. Bridgnorth, Salop. Frances Pitt.

Stomach full of wasp larvae and comb.

A second method is to analyse the droppings. Now in the case of birds, where the intestine is relatively shorter and digestion of certain substances less complete, it is possible to analyse the contents more accurately. In my opinion, however, it is not possible in the case of the badger to get reliable figures of the proportion of animal to vegetable matter by this means. All that can be done is to see the frequency of the various substances. It is also not possible to find any trace of soft-bodied animals like worms and slugs. Fur of rabbits and bone fragments can be seen, and the cuticular structure of insects. Vegetable matter is at times fairly obvious, but it cannot be analysed in detail.

I have analysed the droppings on numerous occasions over several years, and, as far as the limitations of the method allow, the results give a good idea of seasonal change in the diet of the badger. The method employed was to wash out the dung in coarse hessian or a sieve, and place the remainder in white dishes in clean water for examination. In order to make the results clearer I have in the following table arranged the cases in order of time of year, but irrespective of the year in which they were carried out. I have also incorporated the analyses carried out by Gwion Davies (1936) near Denbigh to make it as comprehensive as possible. When examining the table, it is important to realize that the dates refer to the time of analysis, which may have been as much as a week later than the time when the food was eaten. Also, when little identifiable remains are found, it suggests a higher proportion of the softer ingredients such as slugs, worms, and the soft parts of animals generally. I have found that this often corresponds to a period of wet weather.

DUNG ANALYSIS

Date	Material	Authority
Jan. 1	Vegetable remains. Little recognizable.	E. G. N.
,, 6	Rabbit fur from old rabbit. Two or three small bird feathers. Broken fragments of rodent teeth.	,,
,, 8	A great quantity of vegetable material including much grass, leaves, acorns (few).	,,
,, 19	Entirely vegetable remains, much of it grass.	,,
Feb. 9	Vegetable remains. Little recognizable.	,,
,, 20	Vegetable remains. Little recognizable.	,,
March 5	Remains of thorax and back of adult rabbit – ribs and vertebrae only.	,,
,, 10	Beetle elytra and legs. Some vegetable matter.	,,
,, 21	Beetle elytra. Vegetable matter.	,,
,, 26	Large quantity of vegetable matter, mainly grass. One beetle.	,,
April 5	Beetles. Rabbit fur. Vegetable matter.	,,
,, 10	Beetles. Rabbit fur. Broken fragments of rabbit skull.	,,

DUNG ANALYSIS (*continued*)

Date	Material	Authority
April 27	Large number of beetles including *Geotrupes, Melolontha, Carabus*.	E.G.N.
	Young rabbit fur. Leg bones of young rabbit. Small proportion of vegetable matter.	,,
April ?	Fragments of scaly skin of small bird's foot. Quantity of fragments of small jaw bones with teeth 11 and 16 mm. long. Incisor teeth of young rabbits.	Gwion Davies
May 8	Beetles. Vegetable remains in large amounts.	E.G.N.
,, 16	Little recognizable. Some vegetable matter.	,,
June 10	Much fibrous vegetable matter.	,,
,, 20	Little recognizable.	,,
,, 26	Rabbit fur, beetle elytra.	,,
July 2	Little recognizable. Some plant matter.	,,
,, 25	Rabbit fur, some plant matter.	,,
,, 31	Beetle elytra. Rabbit fur.	,,
Aug. 3	Oats. Few beetle elytra.	,,
,, 5	Oats. Beetle elytra.	,,
,, 6	Corn. Rabbit fur. Beetles.	,,
,, 10	Beetles and corn.	,,
,, 11	Beetles. Corn. Rabbit fur.	,,
,, 13	Beetles. Rabbit fur.	,,
,, 25	Beetles. Much plant material.	,,
,, ?	Great quantity of beetle remains (*Geotrupes*). Three or four larva skins. Few incisors of very young rabbits. 1-cm. bird quill. Quantity of short rabbit fur. Plant debris including largely husks of wheat and oats.	Gwion Davies

DUNG ANALYSIS (*continued*)

Date	Material	Authority
Sept. 1	Plant material. Beetles. Rabbit fur.	E.G.N.
„ 2	Corn husks.	„
„ 10	Blackberries much in evidence. Beetles.	„
„ 10	Beech mast. Acorns.	„
„ 12	Beetles, mainly *Geotrupes*.	„
„ 15	Beetles. Rabbit fur.	„
Oct. 3	Beetles in numbers.	„
„ 12	Vegetable matter mainly. Few beetles.	„
„ 24	Vegetable remains. Little recognizable.	„
Nov. 18	Vegetable remains. Little recognizable.	„
Dec. 10	Vegetable matter.	„
„ 21	Vegetable matter.	„
„ 23	Vegetable matter mainly. Woodlice.	„
„ 30	Vegetable matter.	„
„ ?	Mainly vegetable remains and rabbit hair. Also acorn shells. Skin of bird's foot with toes 19 and 15 mm. long. Bird's quill 14 mm. × 1 mm. About 8·6 sq. cm. of broken white eggshell half the thickness of hen's egg. A few splintered bird bones 5 mm. in diameter and a larva skin.	Gwion Davies

A third method of studying the badger's food is simply to watch the animals eating. This is not so simple, really; indeed, it is seldom possible, but occasionally food material has been directly recognized in this way – for instance, snails, bark off trees, various forms of low herbage, wasps and bees. Further reference will be made to these later.

A fourth method is to see what badgers prefer when in captivity. This is, of course, not necessarily the same as they would eat in the wild, but it throws an important light on the sort of food they are fond of, and what they will not touch. Howard Lancum tells me his pet badger cubs have eaten beetles of many kinds, wasps and wasp grubs, rabbits, potato, turnip and mangold (rarely), porridge, bread and milk, bacon rind (in small quantities), windfall apples (occasionally), slugs, snails, grass roots, and various roots and berries. They never touch carrion of any kind.

Dr T.A. Sprague told me an amusing story of how, when motoring near Colesbourne, Glos., he came upon four young badger cubs trotting down the lane in broad daylight. He could not stop, but on his return the cubs were still there and some village children were feeding them on buns! The parents had presumably been killed, so the cubs, which were very young, had left the set to fend for themselves.

I propose now to comment upon the various foods eaten by badgers, or said to be eaten by them. To do this I shall classify the foods according to the natural classification. Small or young mammals are commonly eaten, but large ones are seldom attacked in this country. The following are among the more important.

Rabbits undoubtedly are the badger's main animal food in most parts of the country. Their fur is noticeable in the dung at most seasons of the year, though it is much more common during the months when young rabbits are available. The badger gets young rabbits by locating the position of the nest with its nose, and then digging vertically downwards, the shortest but not the most obvious route. In the season it is not unusual to come upon these excavated nests. No other animal digs them up in this way. In districts where vegetable material is scarcer the badger relies more and more on rabbits. This is very true of the more hilly or mountainous districts. Old rabbits are normally not attacked. I have many times seen rabbits and badgers within sight of each other, but I have never seen a badger pay the slightest attention to one. A rabbit is much faster than a badger and can easily get away. If a rabbit is caught in a trap, however, or is wounded in some way, then a badger may eat one. Frances Pitt (1933) writes in this connexion, 'A badger will pull rabbit after rabbit out of the wires and leave only skins turned neatly inside out.' However, the badger sometimes swallows the fur of adult rabbits (which I have seen in dung on 6 January), and usually swallows at least some of the fur of young. (See table on next page.)

In districts where badgers are plentiful they must certainly play an important part in keeping the numbers of rabbits down.

Rats are also eaten, dead or alive. A local farmer told me that his men were once threshing a rick which contained a large number of rats, many of which were killed. As it was late by the time they had finished, he put the dead rats in a pile intending to bury them the next morning; but badgers during the night came upon this heap and ate all the rats. Only the pad marks of the badgers all around remained to tell the tale. By the number of naturalists who have identified rats as food of badgers there seems little doubt that they are eaten quite often. (See table overleaf.)

Mice and voles are also eaten. Mortimer Batten (1923) tells how he came upon a place where an extensive burrow of the water-vole had been dug up. Among the ruins he found the tails and part of the skins of one or two of the voles. Badger prints were everywhere, showing what animal was responsible for the deed.

Moles and hedgehogs are eaten by badgers. A. H. Cocks (1903–4) comments specially on their liking for the former. Hedgehogs are certainly a favourite food. The four adults in the stomach examined by A. D. Middleton provide excellent evidence for that. In addition it is not at all unusual to find the skin of a hedgehog with the meat removed left flattened and on its back. This is certainly the work of a badger.

What about lambs? Lamb-killing is one of the most serious charges laid at the badger's door. How much truth is there in the accusation? There are cases of lambs being killed by badgers, but they are so rare that I know of no British naturalist who has ever known of one from first-hand experience. In fact the only record I can find where the evidence is adequate

ANIMAL FOOD RECORDED

	F. Pitt, 1935, 1938, 1941	M. Batten, 1923, 1925	G. Davies, 1936	Fairfax-Blakeborough, 1914	C. Vogt, 1887	A. Pease, 1895
MAMMALS						
Young rabbits	C	C	C	X		
Old rabbits	X		CX			
Rats		X		X	X	
Mice					X	
Voles		X				
Hedgehogs		X		X		
Moles					X	
Dead lamb				X		
Live lamb		X				
BIRDS						
Adults			X		X	
Eggs			X	X	X	
REPTILES						
Snakes	X				X	
Lizards					X	
AMPHIBIANS						
Frogs	X					
Toads					X	
MOLLUSCS						
Slugs	X					O
Snails	X				X	O
CRUSTACEANS						
Woodlice						
INSECTS						
Bees and larvae	X		C	X	X	
Wasps	X		X	X	X	
Lepidopterous larvae			X		X	
Other larvae					X	
Beetles			C			
Worms			X		X	X

Notes: X denotes a food recorded but with no indication of frequency.

AS EATEN BY BADGERS

H.Lancum, 1945	L.E.Cheeseman, 1920	T.Hyde Parker, 1941	E.Hardy, 1944	A.H.Cocks, 1903	E.G.Neal	Comment
C		X	C	X	C	Very commonly
O			X	C	R	Occasionally
		X	C		X	Commonly
X		X	X	X		Commonly
X						Occasionally
			X		X	Occasionally
				C		Occasionally
						Rarely
						Very rarely indeed
O			O		R	Very occasionally
O				X		Occasionally
				X		Rarely
				X		Rarely
X		X	O	X		Occasionally
	X					Rarely
X		X	O	X	C	Commonly
X		X	O		X	Occasionally
					R	One occasion only
		X	X	X	X	Commonly
C		X	X	X	X	Commonly
				X		Occasionally
			X		X	Occasionally
C		X	X	X	C	Very commonly
		X		X	C	Commonly

C = Commonly.   R = Rarely.   O = Occasionally.

PLANT FOOD RECORDED

	F.Pitt, 1935, 1938, 1941	M.Batten, 1923, 1925	G.Davies, 1936	Fairfax-Blakeborough, 1914	C.Vogt, 1887	A.Pease, 1895
FRUITS (Gen.)					X	
Acorns			X	X		
Beech nut						
Blackberries						
Apples						
Corn			X			
ROOTS AND STORAGE ORGANS		X	X	X		
Bluebell bulbs						
Cuckoo pint						
Pig-nut						
BARK						
HERBACEOUS PLANTS						
Grass						
Wild parsley						
Dog's mercury						
FUNGI					X	

Notes: X denotes a food recorded but with no indication of frequency.

was recounted by Mortimer Batten. He said, 'A North Wales proprietor informed me that several lambs were killed on his property, and that foxes were thought to be responsible. One night, however, two of the dogs attacked and held something while the shepherd was on his round, and after a terrific struggle, in which the man lent able assistance, the badger, for such it was, was killed. The animal was found covered with blood and a newly-killed lamb was found at the point from which it had started.' Other cases have been reported, some of which were afterwards proved to be wrong, while others were inconclusive. Now, if a badger came across

AS EATEN BY BADGERS

H. Lancum, 1945	L. E. Cheeseman, 1920	T. Hyde Parker, 1941	E. Hardy, 1944	A. H. Cocks, 1903	E. G. Neal	Comment
X			X		X	Commonly
					X	Commonly
					X	
			X		X	Occasionally
X					X	Occasionally
			X	X	X	Occasionally
X	X				X	Commonly
	X				X	
	X					
	X					
					X	Occasionally
X					X	Commonly in winter
	X					
					X	
X		X				

C = Commonly.   R = Rarely.   O = Occasionally.

a dead lamb, or one killed by a fox, I think it might eat it, but if it did, it would certainly eat it on the spot. Mortimer Batten writes along similar lines, 'I have never known badgers drag food into their burrows, certainly not the sort of food that would make the warren foul, whereas foxes habitually do.' Again he states, 'Badgers are not lamb killers, though individuals, if they have found dead lambs lying about, may attack living ones; if so, they kill by biting behind the shoulder and leave it where killed.' Frances Pitt holds the same view. She writes, 'To say that no badger has ever killed a lamb would be going too far, but I do state positively that no iota of evidence has ever come my way. In a case where a lamb's skin was found before the entrance of a set, examination showed a vixen and cubs were lying in part of the burrow, and that the vixen had picked up and brought home a still-born lamb. In my experience the badger never carries home food of any description, and when remnants are discovered about the earth, it will be found foxes have been lying in it.'

Foxes habitually live for short or long periods in badger sets, and this fact is responsible for nearly all the accounts of 'badgers killing lambs'. The evidence is nearly always the presence of lamb remnants outside the set, but it is the fox and not the badger that has brought them there. To make the generalization that badgers kill lambs is completely absurd; probably not one killing a year takes place in Britain.

Another accusation brought against the badger is that it kills poultry and game birds. I have not come across a single instance myself of a badger killing poultry, though it is quite certain that it does so on occasion. Frances Pitt writes in this connexion, 'Although badgers are so plentiful in my home district, although poultry-keeping is practised on a large scale, and the fowls are often housed close to occupied badger sets, I have never met with a single instance of a badger interfering with them. As I am intimately connected with the pack of hounds that hunt this area, and damage by foxes comes too often to my notice, I should know of any raid by badgers.'

The chauffeur at Eycot House, Rendcomb, described how he was awakened by a great commotion going on in the hen house. On opening the door of the hut, a badger came out, but to his surprise he found all the hens unharmed.

Gwion Davies reports three instances of badger raids on poultry in an area round Denbigh where poultry are plenti-ful. One of these he related as follows: 'Mr Jackson, keeper of Galltfaenan, put four hens under a coop in a fenced-off spinney. All were carried off, the coop being overturned. Soon after he found a hen dying inside a coop in a wired and netted hen run, with a torn throat and exposed wind pipe. There were marks on the wall of the coop like those made by a badger. Next evening and following morning he waited in the paddock and shot a badger inside it. Afterwards no hens were taken.' Gwion Davies adds that in the district there were many other cases of nearness of poultry to badgers when hens were *not* attacked.

I have recently been told on reliable evidence of poultry-killing by badgers when the animal has been caught in the act. These reports came from Ireland, South Wales, Somerset, and Kent. On analysing the circumstances of all cases that have come to my notice, I cannot help coming to the conclusion that poultry-killing occurs either in February and March, when this coincides with hard weather, or in places where badgers are very numerous locally. In the first case they would be suckling young cubs and the normal food of the parents would be hard to obtain, and in the second, food would again be difficult to get, this time owing to numbers. Very occasionally you get an old badger which 'goes wrong', just as you do with dogs, and poultry are attacked; but I am convinced that the majority of badgers never attack poultry.

The most reliable evidence of all that poultry-killing is a rare happening was given me by Howard Lancum, who is ornithologist and press officer to the Ministry of Agriculture. He wrote as follows: 'Having in twenty-five years investigated a hundred cases of fowl killing, having in only two of such cases found the badger guilty, and those in very exceptional circumstances; having further in no less than eighty-three of these cases found foxes to be the culprits beyond any reasonable doubt, I have no difficulty in giving my own opinion as to the position of the badger *vis-à-vis* the poultry farmer.'

In my experience gamekeepers are almost all of the opinion that badgers will kill sitting game and eat the eggs, but on being questioned I have never known one give reliable evidence for saying so. I have little doubt in my own mind that if a badger, in the course of nosing around for food, came across a nest of eggs it would eat them, but actual evidence is hard to come by and there are many instances of broods being successfully reared by pheasants nesting within a very short distance of occupied badger sets. Gwion Davies says he had identified broken pheasant eggs among the stomach contents of a badger killed near Denbigh. This is one of the few pieces of reliable evidence I have come across.

I am quite convinced myself that a badger is not really interested in adult birds unless it is very hungry. The only evidence I have come across myself has been the presence of two or three feathers in the droppings on January 6 following a very hard spell of frost. They were of the starling size, and I would guess that in nosing under the bushes the badger had found a dead bird killed by the heavy frost. Gwion Davies mentions the remains of several birds mainly of small size, also in the middle of winter.

Reptiles and Amphibia do not figure largely in the badger's diet, and I have no instances to record myself. However, snakes, lizards, frogs, and toads have all been reported on reliable authority. A. H. Cocks (1903–4) tells how a badger eats frogs: 'The badger holds down the unlucky frog with one fore foot, then literally scrubs it to death with the palm of the other foot ... the object being apparently to get rid of the secretion of slime.' He also states that 'snakes and lizards were also eaten in captivity.'

Molluscs are commonly eaten, specially slugs. These I have found in most stomach contents I have examined. I have heard badgers scrunching up snails – a sound that cannot be confused with anything else!

Badgers have little chance of eating crustaceans; but one of the only terrestrial British representatives, the woodlouse, is eaten as I have found its remains in their droppings on one occasion.

Insects have such hard exoskeletons that their indigestible remains are easily recognized. They are eaten in large numbers. It is probably true to say that a badger in the course of its rootings will eat most insects it finds which are of a reasonable size. Those most commonly taken are beetles, lepidopterous larvae, bees, and wasps.

In my experience the beetles most often eaten belong to the genus *Geotrupes* (Dor-beetles), those large blundering black beetles with a bluish sheen which fly with a droning sound at dusk. Other types of dung-beetle are also eaten including those of the genus *Aphodius*, and observations during the day demonstrate where the dung of cattle and horses has been overturned by badgers when searching for these creatures. Howard Lancum tells me they are very fond of May-bugs (*Melolontha*), and Dr Colin Matheson tells me, how, during a plague of cockchafer grubs in Monmouthshire, 'an entomologist friend who was investigating the problem noticed that the Badgers were coming down at night and feeding on the grubs, no doubt getting rid of large numbers.' I have come across the elytra of a number of ground-beetles including those of the genera *Carabus* and *Pterostichus* in the droppings. Certain of the large Staphylinids are also eaten. The presence of beetle remains is definitely seasonal. They can occur commonly from March to October, but there is usually a falling-off in the number during May, June, and July.

Caterpillars are not despised, and I once found the perfect skin of a hawk-moth larva in some droppings one September. Noctuid larvae are of frequent occurrence; this is understandable as many of them are nocturnal and feed on low herbage and would therefore come within reach of a prowling badger.

Wasps' nests are prime favourites with badgers, and anybody who has been fortunate enough to see a badger attacking one is hardly likely to forget the experience. The badger becomes very excited, and heedless of the angry swarm of wasps that buzz around it and settle on its coat and face, it digs furiously, scattering the earth far and wide. Its main object is to eat the fat larvae, but adults are also snapped up. Pieces of comb are scattered all over the place.

Howard Lancum tells me how the village boys used to come round and ask if they could borrow his pet badger to seek out wasps' nests in the autumn. They would take it out on a lead and when in the vicinity of a nest they would let it off the lead. The excited animal would make quick work of the nest.

W. C. J. R. Butterworth (1905) writes: 'In 1893, a great wasp year, the badgers at Beauport (Sussex) devoured between them thirty to forty wasps' nests during two ensuing nights.' I have known many nests ravaged in this way, and there is no doubt that badgers account for a great number.

Bees' nests are also greatly appreciated by badgers. The added attraction of the honey makes them, if anything, more of a delicacy than a wasps' nest. They eat the adults, larvae, and comb. I am indebted to the editor of the *Countrygoer* for allowing me to quote from an interesting article in which B. Melville Nicholas (1946) gives an eye-witness account of a badger's attack on a bees' nest in broad daylight. He had erected a hide to photograph a sitting woodcock, 'which had laid her eggs on the bare ground only a few feet from a well-worn badger track. Suddenly the white striped face of a badger appeared, passed quite close to the woodcock's nest, and then stopped. For seconds he stood motionless without even blinking an eyelid, and then I noticed there were hundreds of honey bees swarming around him. They had escaped from an apiary and, unfortunately for them, the badger had discovered their nest at the foot of a fir tree. From where I sat in my "hide" I watched him callously rip off the bark with his strong jaws and ravenously feast on the honey. Meanwhile the angry bees swarmed round the robber in thousands, trying in vain to drive in their stings, but the badger remained unaffected and, at the rate he was eating, must surely have devoured many bees as well as the honey. Once or twice he raised his paw to brush the furious insects from his face, as the honey trickled down over his jaws. Eventually, as though suddenly seized by fear, the badger left the feast and departed at an amazing speed to his set. The reason for this sudden and rapid rush homewards I never discovered, although it was just possible that one of the bees found a tender spot.'

In Denbigh, Gwion Davies found three ravaged bees' nests with badger hairs lodged in the heap of loose earth thrown out. Raided nests were also found by five other sets but no badger hairs could be seen. In three cases they were nine inches deep and in clay soil, and would have taken a powerful digger to get at them.

Finally, as far as animal food is concerned, I must mention earthworms. These are certainly eaten in large numbers, especially on wet nights when the worms lie on the surface of the grass.

1. Adult Badger. Flashlight Photograph. Somerset, April

2. Conigre Wood, Rendcomb: aerial photograph with the Cheltenham-Cirencester road on the right. November

3. Earth and bedding: a great heap outside a set. Eycot, Gloucestershire, March

4. Adult waiting by its set. Eycot, Gloucestershire, August

5. Badger sniffing the air before cautiously emerging from its set.
Cheshire, August

6. Three adults and a cub (aged about twelve weeks) near the set
entrance. Eycot, Gloucestershire, May

7. The very yellow female (right), her two cubs (six months old), and a stranger (back view), at set C. Conigre wood, Gloucestershire, August

8. Boldly coming out of the set. Cheshire, September

9. Listening and suspicious with paw raised. Cheshire, July

10. Leaving set C. Conigre wood, Gloucestershire, August

11. Young badger at the set entrance. Breconshire, August

12. Sharpening its claws on a tree. Somerset, August

14. Investigating set B. Conigre wood, Gloucestershire, September

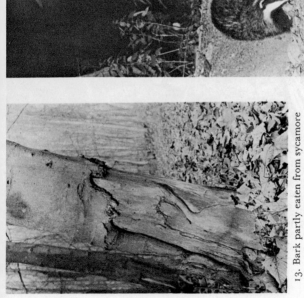

13. Bark partly eaten from sycamore tree by badgers. Conigre wood, Gloucestershire, October

15. Boar (right), sow (centre), a third adult, and two cubs. Eycot,
Gloucestershire, May

16. Playing on a favourite tree stump near set A. Conigre wood,
Gloucestershire, September

17. A set entrance, showing bedding dropped on the right. Eycot, Gloucestershire, September

18. A set in winter, showing signs of considerable activity. Radnorshire, February

19. Cub about three months old. Radnorshire, May

20. Cubs approximately twelve weeks old. County Down, July

21. Sow and two cubs. County Down, July

22. Four badgers playing: the one on the left is playfully biting its neighbour. Eycot, Gloucestershire, August

23. Five adults from one set. Eycot, Gloucestershire, August

24. Playing leap-frog. Radnorshire, July

25. Two badgers: the one on the left is removing a large stone from the
set while the other is sliding down the bank. Cheshire, September

26. A typical badger set with a well-worn path leading up the bank to the
right. Chisfield Park, East Anglia, July

27. Emerging at dusk. County Down, August

28. Returning home: muddy after grubbing for food.
Radnorshire, August

29. A large badger seen close up. Radnorshire, August

30. German engraving by J. E. Ridinger (1698-1769) of a badger
and its spoor

Now let us consider plant food. Badgers will eat many kinds of fruits, probably the majority of succulent fruits they are able to reach. I have been able to identify acorns, beech-mast, blackberries, windfall apples, and corn. Acorn and beech-mast fragments are commonly found in the droppings during the autumn, and I have found quantities of the former in a stomach analysis. Blackberries are easily identified by the colour and pips, and they are not infrequently eaten in September.

I have only noticed windfall apples on one occasion and the evidence was only circumstantial. By one set in the Cotswolds there was a large apple tree growing and the ground was strewn with windfalls. Some of these were much eaten, and the tooth marks appeared to be those of a large animal, certainly not a rodent. Howard Lancum says they will eat windfalls while cubs under domestication.

Corn husks are occasionally found in the droppings of badgers, though I have only noted it when the corn field has been very near the set, usually bordering the wood in which the set was located. I have only found it in August, the time when the corn is cut, never before. I have heard it said by farmers that badgers will trample down corn to get at the ears to eat them, but it is my belief that this is not so. When it is in stook, or lying on the ground, they will certainly do some gleaning if they happen to be near, but when they do batter down corn (it does happen occasionally) I think it is certainly due to their playing and romping and has nothing to do with their feeding. Badgers often have regular playing grounds which they keep to year after year; in Conigre they beat down the rosebay every year during July or August, during this season of romping when the cubs are getting big. If a farmer grows corn near a wood containing badgers it may well be that part of his field will coincide with one of their playgrounds, so the corn gets battered down. The damage done in this way is very small. A local squire whom I questioned about this because I knew he had had experience of it, gave it as his opinion that less corn was lost in this way than through the thresher.

Roots and underground storage organs probably form an important proportion of a badger's diet during the autumn

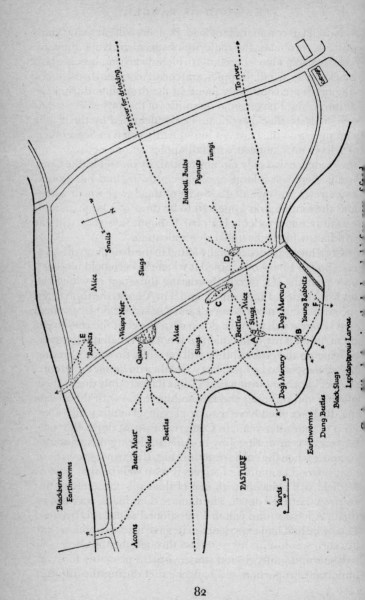

To river for drinking

To river

Snails

Bluebell Bulbs

Fungi

Mice

Slugs

N

Wasps' Nest

Mice

Slugs

Quarry

Beech Mast

Voles

Beetles

Beetles

Mice

Slugs

A

C

D

E

Rabbits

Dog's Mercury

Young Rabbits

F

B

Dog's Mercury

Lepidopterous Larvae

Black Slugs

Earthworms

Dung Beetles

PASTURE

Blackberries

Earthworms

Acorns

Yards
0   10   20

82

and winter. Fibrous material is commonly found in the stomach or droppings of badgers at this time of the year. Many times I have seen where badgers have been rooting for these succulent organs in the cold weather when other material was difficult to get. They are usually impossible to identify specifically, but bluebell bulbs and the rhizomes and storage roots of woodland plants figure largely.

Very occasionally badgers become a nuisance by rooting about in gardens or allotments after vegetables. There is one remarkable set within the city boundaries of Gloucester. A housing estate had enclosed an area in which a flourishing badger set had been for many generations. The soil was sandy and the tunnels went in a great distance, preventing people from digging them out. At night these badgers would occasionally dig up vegetables, but who could blame them? After all, they were there first and man was the trespasser! There is no doubt, however, that these cases were very exceptional. Under normal circumstances food is sufficiently plentiful near at hand for them to feed to repletion without having to go out of their way for vegetables.

I referred (p. 64) to a roll of sycamore bark which I found in the stomach of a dead badger. This is of considerable interest as regards the harm badgers do or do not do to trees. I have heard on many occasions the statement that badgers destroy trees and do a lot of harm to saplings by stripping the bark. Now, it is one of the obvious signs of a well-established set that, if there are trees in the vicinity, some may show the bark partially stripped off them to a height of about two feet. It has been said by some that this is due to the constant scraping of claws by badgers either in stretching and sharpening claws, or cleaning the feet when muddy. Others take the view that the badger bites the bark off. Having watched them at work on numerous occasions I have no doubt how it is done. There is always one tree, usually within a yard or so of the set entrance, which the badgers use for stretching and claw-scraping. On emerging at dusk, and after a good scratch, a badger will approach the tree, get up on its hind legs, reach up the trunk to its full height and bring the claws downwards.

The habit is so usual that the mud marks on the trunk are easily seen in the day-time. But on these trees the bark is always intact. I have, however, seen a badger on a few occasions eat the bark off a tree. I have noted the date whenever I have noticed fresh bark removed: on every occasion it has been in early spring, and I am convinced that a badger does this to get at the sweet sap that exudes from the exposed parts at this time of year. The trees treated in this way are usually sycamores and beeches. The actual damage to the tree, in my experience, is negligible, and I have never known a tree killed as a result. As to saplings, I do not consider the badger is interested; the meal would not be worth the trouble, and I have no evidence of damage. Almost all the cases of bark removed from saplings that I have come across were due to rabbits or grey squirrels.

A certain amount of green herbage is eaten. I have identified grasses and dog's mercury shoots, and a few leaves of other plants. I have no evidence myself that badgers eat fungi, but Vogt (1887) mentions that truffles are eaten, and Hyde Parker (1941) also makes reference to fungi.

To sum up: the badger is truly omnivorous, and is far more interested in small food than large. It seeks eagerly, here, there, and everywhere for anything edible it can find; worms, insects, a nest of young rabbits, or, with luck, a wasps' nest. As you watch it searching, it will root about like a pig for hidden delicacies, making a dart after some more active little animal, or with eager grunts digging for bluebell bulbs or pig-nuts. These are its normal foods. Rarely, and under exceptional circumstances, a badger may take to killing poultry or even a lamb, but this is no more typical of the species than highway robbery is typical of man.

The number of insect pests and vermin that a badger destroys must be very large indeed, and when badgers are plentiful they certainly help to keep the numbers of rabbits within reasonable bounds. There is not the slightest doubt that the badger is a real friend to the farmer.

There is one question that is often asked: do badgers kill fox cubs? This is not a question of food, as they are never eaten. However, I will discuss the question briefly in this chapter. Many cases have been reported of fox cubs lying outside earths or badger sets bitten to death but not eaten. The badger has been blamed for this deed. This is a very old bone of contention, and a long correspondence about it appeared in the *Field* towards the end of the last century. There were many opinions given, but little more than circumstantial evidence elicited. I think myself that it is quite possible that very occasionally a badger may kill fox cubs, but it is equally likely, if not more so, that it is the work of an old dog-fox or a barren vixen, the latter being much more probable. The matter is by no means settled, but, when dealing with wild animals, which probably differ in their mental make-up nearly as much as we do ourselves, exceptions to the general rule are likely to turn up from time to time. To say that a badger often kills fox cubs is absurd; that a rogue badger, under exceptional circumstances, may do so is possible. That is as far as I can go.

CHAPTER 6

GENERAL BEHAVIOUR

THE behaviour of an animal may be described as the sum of its responses to the conditions and circumstances of its environment. A badger lives in a world very different from ours. We live in a world of colour, a world where sight plays such an important part. A badger sees a monochrome world (it probably lacks colour vision); it comes out of its set when light is nearly gone; it is more at home in a dark tunnel than in the brightness of sunlight.

What senses are most important in the life of a badger? As it is a nocturnal animal you would not expect sight to play much part in its life; but it is unwise to jump to conclusions, as some crepuscular animals have extremely good eyesight. The general look of those small, rather pig-like eyes, however, suggests that the badger relies more on his other senses. This is borne out by many observations.

While watching badgers I usually stand with my back to a tree-trunk, if this is available, or sit quietly in front of a bush. In the dusk this gives the badgers no silhouette, but in midsummer, when they emerge in good light within fifteen feet of me, they should be able to see me with ease, as I never use camouflage or a hide. Their reactions are nearly always the same if I am right as regards the wind. On emerging, the first badger will sniff carefully in all directions with its snout raised; if it gets no scent to worry it, it will sit at the mouth of its set and have a good look round. When it looks in my direction, it will stop and stare. Two things may happen now: either it will retire slowly underground, or else, seeing no movement, it will sit and watch for a few minutes, then, apparently satisfied, it will scratch and take no further notice of me. But if I make the slightest movement, it will plunge for its set and not return for a very long time, probably not at all that night if I happen to be watching a strange set. If, however, it retires slowly, having seen no movement, it will soon try again when the light is poorer, and this time will probably stay out.

The badger's sight, therefore, appears to be excellent for detecting movement of any kind. The picture of me sitting there with the midges playing havoc with my skin gives the badger no danger associations, and it accepts me as part of the landscape. It appears to me that, as a badger builds up a fund of experience, associating facts about food or danger with specific stimuli, it soon gets used to the surroundings to its set, the trees and bushes, their shapes and position; it sees these often, but how can it associate man with that shape in front of the tree? The animal has never connected that sight with danger, so why should it worry? But when I move it is very different. All movement may be dangerous, and I suspect that in the badger's brain the sight of any sudden and unexpected movement is inheritably linked with a danger-reaction. Later it learns that some movements are not dangerous. A badger cub, for example, will rush headlong for the set if a rabbit, which it has not noticed sitting quietly near by, gives a jump, but an adult will take no notice.

A badger, when it looks at you, will see but not understand; the unusualness of the situation will make it wary; it sees the possibility of danger, but that is all.

There was one instance I shall never forget when even movement had no effect on a badger's reactions. A local wood had been cut down during the First World War, and young ash trees had grown up in profusion in its place. By 1944 there was an impenetrable thicket of bramble between the trees. There was a large set in this wood in a part where the undergrowth was very thick. The badger roads radiating out from it were tunnels rather than paths. I hacked my way through one day, and decided to try for a photograph. The difficulty was that I could not get a vantage point far enough away. In the end I had to focus from seven feet. A badger emerged at late dusk and stared at me – with my camera on a tripod in front of me and a reflector and flash bulb in place. It stared and stared. I took a photograph and it turned as if to go down its set; but it changed its mind and just sat there. I wound on my film and changed the bulb, but still it sat on, two yards or so away. I took another photograph – another blinding flash – but still no headlong rush for home. This time, in changing the bulb, I made quite a lot of noise; it took a pace towards me, gave me a last look, and then ambled off, its curiosity apparently satisfied. It was an astonishing experience. That this animal had never seen man before I am certain, as it looked like a last year's cub; and I am sure that nobody had cut his way to this set for several years. There was no sign of fear in the badger, only intense curiosity.

These instances point to the conclusion that badgers perceive much more with their senses other than sight; which is not surprising in a nocturnal animal that lives much of its life in a labyrinth of dark tunnels. Several times in the dusk I have stood still on a badger path and watched one come sniffing along towards me. If the wind has been in my favour it has come within a yard of my feet before it has realized my presence; if it had been *looking* where it was going it could not have failed to see me.

The badger's sense of smell is very acute. In my opinion it is by far its most important sense. A successful badger-watching expedition depends more on the direction of the wind than on any other single factor. I have had badgers romping at my feet in good light when the wind has been blowing in my face. I have watched within six feet of a set's entrance in a new locality and seen a boar bringing in bedding within a yard of where I was standing, with the wind, again, just right. But the faintest breeze at your back, or a variable one which comes in eddies, and the badgers are suspicious at once; all you may see is a striped snout at the entrance and then no more.

Badgers can detect where a person has been walking some time after he has passed. I well remember one occasion when I was watching a set in June. I had come by a somewhat circuitous route to the vantage point I had chosen, and after half an hour no badger had emerged. It was not long, however, before I heard the familiar rattle of loose stones as a badger approached from another set. Soon I could see it clearly, nose to earth as it padded towards me. It did not pause until it reached the exact spot where I had crossed its path about half an hour before. It stopped dead, sniffed hard with snout raised, and then backed slowly. Hesitatingly it took a few steps to the right and again approached, with the same result. It then dashed across to the set entrance some ten yards farther on and went down at once. This type of thing has happened many times. On one occasion when a boy was some distance up a tree, a badger came unconcernedly to the trunk, only to dash away on sniffing the bark. The boy was much too high to be scented directly from below, but in getting up the tree enough scent was left to give him away.

Badgers are said to locate the exact position of the nests of young rabbits by scent. This is almost certainly true, though difficult to prove. It is characteristic of them to dig vertically down to the nest, rather than enlarge one of the entrances and get to it by the longer but more obvious route.

I have tried to determine roughly the distance a badger is away from me when he first detects my scent, when the wind has been blowing slightly but definitely from me towards it. On about eight occasions I have been able to note this – almost always when I have been watching set C and a badger has come from A and approached from behind. The badger usually comes at an ambling trot, approaching to within ten yards before stopping short with snout raised. Then it usually retires rapidly in the opposite direction. This comparatively short distance has surprised me. It may be that when its nose is near the ground other smells tend to overcome the direct wind-borne scent. I am certain that if a badger were emerging from its set with its nose in the air, it would scent me from much further off if the wind were in its favour.

At certain seasons of the year the sensitivity to scent stimuli is greatly increased, especially in the female. I have found this most marked when cubs are either about to be born or are still very small. I watched at C on a number of occasions in February to see the behaviour of a pair which I anticipated would have cubs at about that time. The boar would invariably come out first and usually go off quite quickly to the feeding grounds without scenting me at all. But when the sow emerged she was supersensitive and although I was right for wind as I thought, she was greatly suspicious when I was near and would retreat on the slightest provocation.

On 27 February I was watching at A where there was a pair with two cubs, afterwards calculated to be two to three weeks old at this time. When the boar emerged it waited some time for the sow, but, getting impatient, moved off along a track towards B. When it reached a point opposite to where I was standing – a distance of about fifteen feet – it stopped and sniffed, then went unconcernedly on. As it was going, the sow came out and followed at once along the same track. At the same spot she also stopped and sniffed, but, unlike the boar, turned round and swiftly retreated. As conditions appeared to be identical in both cases, it is right to assume, I think, that this was due either to greater sensitivity in the sow or greater caution in response to the stimuli received.

The badger's hearing is acute, but nothing out of the way. I should say it hears rather better than we do, but not as well as a dog or rabbit. Its external ears are, of course, extremely small. This may be a reflection on the badger's powers of hearing or may be an adaptation to burrowing life. When waiting silently in a wood at night your hearing becomes more sensitive. There are fewer sounds to attract your attention, so what you do hear sounds loud. The quick rustle of the leaves as a mouse or vole makes a movement sounds startlingly clear, and soon you can detect quite easily the clumsy movements of a ground-beetle crawling along dry leaves. This, no doubt, a badger can do too. The click of my camera shutter at fifteen feet has at once made them alert, and I have often made slight noises with my tongue to get a group of badgers to stop still for a second while I took a photograph.

The breaking of a twig, or a rustling of some leaves, generally makes a badger alert at once, but these are usual sounds and do not necessarily result in a fear reaction. In the autumn, when the dry leaves have been thick on the ground, I have been able to approach badgers without being discovered. Each step has to be taken slowly and irregular pauses have to be made. The sound by itself is not frightening, but a *regular* sequence of crackles is at once taken as a danger sign. A point in the watcher's favour under these circumstances is the fact that, once a badger is unsuspicious, it will make so much noise itself in the leaves that it has little chance of hearing you if you synchronize your noises carefully with its own.

Badgers are noisy creatures. I have already referred to their excited yelps as they play together; the greater the excitement, the more the noise. It is difficult to describe, but it reminds me more of the sounds puppies make when they are fighting – a high-pitched yelp with a trace of a whine in it at times. The noise is easily recognizable at a hundred yards.

Several writers have referred to the badger's yell. Frances Pitt writes of a voice raised in 'a terrible yell, repeated again and again.' As this occurred in October she thought this was the 'love song' of the badger, and this view is shared by other naturalists. At that time it was considered by many that mating took place at that season. As I will show in a later chapter, it has been established that this is not the mating time, and I think the sound has no sexual significance. The first time I heard this yelling was on 14 March about an hour after dark; it was a blood-curdling noise. I have also heard it in late autumn. During the latter time it may have something to do with the cubs leaving the sets in which they have been brought up. I have some evidence that they do this in October, but whether they are forcibly ejected by their parents I do not know. If the yelling is connected with this summary dismissal, it hardly accounts for my hearing it in March. More observations are needed to clear the matter up. However, a possible explanation may be afforded as a result of Brian Vesey-FitzGerald's observation on a badger's funeral (p. 61). On this occasion he described the cry of the sow as 'a weird cry, half whimper, half howl, shrill for so square a beast, and in the still night so sudden, so eerie, that the hairs on the nape of my neck stiffened involuntarily.'

The boar certainly makes a noise that has a sexual significance. I have heard it on a number of occasions. The first time was on 17 February. It was about this time or a little earlier when cubs were born at C. The boar emerged first and sat by the entrance scratching and apparently waiting about. He then looked down the set and made a vibrating, long-drawn-out, low, purring sound. This was repeated and the sow emerged almost at once. There was a short period of excited play and then they went off together towards the open wood.

I heard the same sound on 27 February when watching at A. The male again emerged first and waited about for a long time; he then went to the entrance and six or seven times repeated this purring sound. On getting no response he trotted off, but he had only got a few yards when the sow emerged and followed him. I heard it again at C on 17 March. On these occasions it was the boar calling the sow. Later in the year two adults were romping excitedly together; suddenly they broke away, then the boar made the purring sound and at once mounted the other as for mating.

A variation of this noise is used by an adult to keep back the cubs from the set entrance. I have heard it made on warm summer evenings when the cubs have been impatient to come out. I noticed it again when a family was playing near me and the mother suddenly approached and realized I was there. She bounded back making this noise and bundled the cubs down the hole in front of her.

When the cubs are very small and before they are allowed above ground, they make high-pitched little squeals. One evening in March I watched the sow come back to the set and disappear. I quickly approached the entrance and could hear these cries as the cubs welcomed her home.

Badgers can recognize the noises made by their own kind. When I was watching a set near Eycot, the boar came out first and went off almost at once. The rest of the family remained by the set, romping in their customary manner. Suddenly there was a crackle of twigs and they all stopped and listened. The noise grew louder, but instead of going below, the sow took a few steps to meet the visitor who turned out to be the returning boar. They rubbed noses and retired underground together.

The movements of a badger are very characteristic. When out on a definite errand it will depart at an ambling trot, head down and with its larger hind-quarters swaying from side to side. Its short legs move rapidly but there are frequent pauses. These are probably necessary as in moving it makes a lot of noise and it uses the pauses for listening. As you hear one coming towards you, the 'pad pad pad pad pad stop, pad pad pad pad pad pad pad stop' is unmistakable. When alarmed, its pace over a short distance is considerable and it plunges down the set with thudding pads and often a skid round the corner.

Badgers are fond of climbing on tree trunks, and have their favourite places for disporting in this way. There is one tree near A which was uprooted in a storm. The main trunk was removed, but the old stock sprouted again to produce eventually several thick boughs. The badgers used to play on this a great deal, and the bark was worn right away in places with the continual working of many feet. I was fortunate to photograph three adults playing on this trunk (Plate 16). They are very agile for their bulk, but I was astonished when I saw one actually climb a tree! By that I do not mean just clamber on a fallen one, but work its way up the trunk, probably after slugs. It was nearly dark when I saw this, and, not being quite sure, I photographed it. On developing the negative I was surprised to see that it was climbing like a bear, with the claws of all four feet gripping the trunk.

It is remarkable the way badgers bring in bedding to line their sleeping chambers. I have now watched them do so on a number of occasions and their technique has always been more or less the same, any variation being due to the type of material used. Badgers seem to have individual preferences as regards the material, though its availability is obviously the most important factor. At A, leaves are used every year in autumn, especially chestnut leaves, which are gathered from under a tree about twenty yards away. At C, moss and rosebay are preferred, and tree leaves hardly touched. At B, dog's mercury is regularly taken in along with tree leaves. At another set I have noted that the badgers always use straw, which is obtained from the roof of a tumbled-down thatched shed put up by a gamekeeper. At Eycot they prefer grass, which they bring back in bundles; and in Monkham bracken is most usual. Occasionally other things are utilized, but not regularly; I once found a lot of wild clematis fruits among the bundles left outside the set.

When bringing in leaves a badger will gather all it can find within a small circle, using its fore-paws to collect them. Having got a good heap, it will cuddle it with its front legs, using its snout to keep it in place, and proceed to shuffle backwards, pausing at intervals. When it reaches the entrance, it disappears backwards down the set. With bracken, much more portable bundles are made, which are carried between chin and fore-paws as before, the animal more or less sliding on its elbows as it goes. Badgers will follow the same path time and time again. When watching at A in October, a badger came in my direction and collected leaves from a point about three yards from me; the next time it emerged it came a little nearer, but still it did not suspect my presence. The third time it came right up to my tree and collected the leaves from within a foot of where I was standing!

They will usually choose dry nights for getting bedding; and in the autumn, if you get a series of really dry days and the leaves begin to get crackly, you can assume with reasonable certainty that, if undisturbed, they will bring in material. There are definite periods of the year when bedding is brought in, but autumn is undoubtedly the chief. They collect it spasmodically from September to the beginning of December (according to the dryness of the season). Badger-diggers in winter have come across small cartloads of bedding lining some of the main chambers. But the collecting of bedding also follows the spring-cleaning of the sets. During this process great masses of material are ejected from the main entrances – largely old bedding mixed with earth – forming a huge heap outside. The first spring-clean takes place, in the Cotswolds, on a moderate scale towards the end of January or early in February. For instance, in the middle of a hard spell of frost and snow, leaves were pushed out on top of the snow on

22 January 1945 at both A and B, and on 1 February some were ejected at C. By the 7th the spring-cleaning was in full swing and a great deal of material, mainly earth, was cast out. This occurred at A, B, and C and was presumably in preparation for the birth of cubs. This statement is based on the facts that all three sets were shown to contain mated pairs and that cubs were later seen there; also that the cubs were born first at A, next at B, and latest at C, and spring-cleaning was started in that order at these three sets. It seems likely that a new chamber is dug out each year into which the sow retires when she drops her cubs.

The next bout of activity was noted at A on 20 February when one entrance was scoured out and a lot of earth and old bedding cast out. It was calculated from data obtained later that the cubs were about fourteen days old at this time. This was followed by a similar action at B and C on 1 March when the cubs were thought to be almost the same age – fourteen days once more. I assume from this that the cleaning was associated with the cubs, and as they got bigger more bedding which had been fouled was removed at fairly regular intervals. Fresh material was constantly brought in to replace this, leaves mainly at A and moss at C. After 26 April, when much dog's mercury was brought in at B, there was a slackening, due probably to the fact that the cubs were regularly above ground and no longer fouled the bedding. (The first cubs were seen near A on 11 April.) Except for a little digging towards the end of June, nothing much happened until 8 July, when there was a burst of activity at all the sets up to the 21st. This spring-clean is of some significance, as it often occurs just before the family moves off to live with a neighbour, and in my opinion this set or part of a set is seldom occupied again until the autumn, when the mated pairs return to take up permanent quarters. This is borne out by counts in three successive years, when it was found that the badgers of Conigre Wood all lived together for some time, mainly for August, the other sets being deserted. In large isolated sets with no outliers, I presume only one part of the extensive underground domain is used, and the rest spring-cleaned and left. If this is so, it provides an excellent means of safeguarding the health of the inmates, especially in relation to parasites.

Freshly-killed badgers are hardly ever infested with parasites, except a few fleas, but those kept for long in captivity usually become verminous and unkempt. This changing of sets, which may take place several times in a season, together with the scouring and removal of old bedding are probably the most important reasons for the remarkable health the badger appears to enjoy.

In August and September great digging operations occur, and new entrances and even new sets may be made during this period. Mated pairs are preparing their winter quarters, but if a set is seen to be cleaned out at this time of year you cannot assume that it is being lived in; it is often being prepared while the owners are living with other badgers not far off. On one dawn in August I watched a badger digging at one of these sets, and was confident that it would stop the day there, but it cleared off when the work was finished, and a full count was recorded from another set that night. It was in August that a new set was dug out in a neighbouring wood, probably by members of the Conigre community. An enormous amount of work was done in a few weeks, and by the end of September there were four entrances each with its pile of earth outside. On watching this set only two badgers were observed; so they were certainly a hard-working couple.

The cleanliness of the badger is one of its most remarkable traits. I have referred in a previous chapter (p. 20) to the way in which the mother will clean her cubs and search for parasites in their fur. Badgers also lick themselves, especially their paws, and it is common to see them doing this outside the set entrance.

Lavatories are to be found within a short distance of each set, though occasionally they may be some distance off. They take the form of a series of small pits dug in the ground, perhaps six or more within a radius of a few square yards. These are filled with excrement and then abandoned for fresh ones. They are not covered up wittingly, but they soon fill with leaves and earth. These plots are changed quite frequently. I have on several occasions found dung in the entrance of a set which was not being used at the time, and several times in rabbit holes, but these are exceptional cases. The cubs, when brought above ground, are soon taught to use these pits, and careful watching of the size of droppings provides a useful clue as to when the cubs *are* above ground.

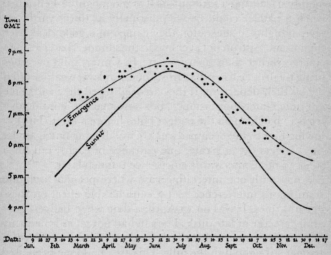

Light intensity and the badger's time of emergence

Badgers, when undisturbed, emerge from their sets at very regular times; this is especially true between March and November. I have noted the time of emergence on most occasions when I have been watching. When these times are plotted against sunset time, it is striking how parallel the curves run during the periods March to May, and August to November. After May, however, badgers tend to come out in much broader daylight, owing no doubt to the shortness of the night necessitating an early start for feeding. During the winter months with the longer hours of darkness, emergence is more irregular, and in late December and January it cannot be forecast with any accuracy. For these months I have not enough data to go on. It can be a chilly business watching for badgers at this time of year for several hours at a time! The time taken in each case is when the first badger has come definitely out of its set.

There seems very little doubt from the graph that light intensity is the most important factor; but other circumstances modify it. During a brilliant spell of moonlight in February, when a badger could be seen distinctly at thirty yards, on several nights in succession they came out a good deal later than usual. Also on hot evenings in the summer, badgers may emerge earlier than is customary. In winter, mild evenings bring them out earlier than frosty ones, and wet weather often delays their departure. If they are frightened they will come out much later. For instance, it is customary in hunting districts to block up all the badger holes before a hunt. The following nights, the occupied sets are usually dug out again by the badgers (at any rate, one entrance of each), but for a week or more afterwards emergence is much later.

I met with one interesting case where peculiar isolation from man's interference had a considerable effect on these general rules. It was on 17 April, a date when badgers generally emerge at late dusk. The sun had not set as I made my way across some chalky down-land in Wiltshire towards a badger stronghold in the hills. This area had long been used as tank country and for artillery practice, but the immediate surroundings of the sets had been at peace from man's interference for a very long time. After walking some distance, avoiding deep tank tracks and barbed wire, I dropped down into one of those surprising pockets in the hills where there was a large strip of woodland. On the far side of the valley, the badger sets showed up plainly. The pure white chalk dug out by the animals seemed to overflow down the hill like milk out of a green jug. It was still broad daylight when I arrived but to my surprise a badger was already out and quietly watching me. It showed no obvious sign of fear, but at my approach regretfully retired down its set. While I was exploring among the clumps of nettles and scattered elders for set entrances, I saw two more adults above ground. The day had been a remarkably hot one for April and this may have been the reason, but I think it more likely that it was the isolation that had brought them out a full hour before the normal time.

CHAPTER 7

HIBERNATION

Do badgers hibernate? The literature on the badger abounds in conflicting statements. Unfortunately, most of the statements are opinions only, and no evidence is given of a reliable kind. It is well to be clear what is implied by hibernation, as the term is very often loosely used. Hibernation means a change in the physiology of the animal which brings about a state of torpor over a considerable period. In cold-blooded animals this is brought about primarily by a drop in the external temperature. As the animals take on the temperature of their surroundings, the vital processes, such as respiration, will slow up considerably and insufficient energy will be released for active living during the winter.

In such mammals as hibernate, hibernation is accompanied by a fall in body temperature, but this is not the direct result of the drop in temperature of the external environment. It may, for example, be due to a change in the amount of a hormone liberated into the blood. Whatever the cause, the whole metabolism of the mammal is undoubtedly altered during hibernation. The oxygen and food requirements of the tissues are slight. The heart beats slowly and almost imperceptibly; breathing is very light, and it is difficult to arouse the animals from their torpor. During hibernation mammals live on food stored in the body, mainly in the form of fat.

Is this in any way true of the badger? Many have stated definitely that they do hibernate, but few try to give evidence. Mortimer Batten (1925) discusses the matter. He states that 'hibernation is more complete than in the case of the squirrel and less complete than in the case of the hedgehog. When badgers are numerous, the tracks of restless individuals are to be seen in the snow through the winter, but it may be taken that for every badger astir in December there are a dozen hibernating ... unless, of course, the winter be an unusually mild one.' I see no evidence from this statement that badgers hibernate. Lazy they may be, but hibernation is surely the wrong word. There is, of course, no doubt that the hedgehog does hibernate, but nobody has found evidence of a squirrel doing so (and there is, indeed, much evidence to the contrary). In fact, as I write this, on the last day of December, I can say that only yesterday I watched for some time two red squirrels chasing each other round a tree; and the tracks of grey squirrels in the snow are a common sight.

In order to clear up the situation, I made a series of observations and tests during the winter of 1944–5. It was certain by November that there were badgers in Conigre Wood in A, B, and C, one pair in each. During November and the first part of December fresh dung was found regularly, and activity was witnessed on a number of occasions. On 10 December all the holes were blocked up for a shoot, but they were unblocked by the badgers at all sets the same night. If they were going to hibernate they should have started doing so by then, but perhaps it was not cold enough.

In the Cotswolds the cold spell started in earnest on Christmas Day with a temperature of 18° F. that night; on Boxing Night there was another heavy frost, and another on the night following. Early the next morning I found fresh unfrozen dung, although everything else was stiff with frost. There were also plenty of signs where the badgers had scraped away the frozen ground to get at the unfrozen earth where food might be found. The spell went on with a frost every night except one, until 6 January. There was such a heavy hoar frost on one occasion that badger tracks could easily be seen round the sets and leading off to other parts of the wood. This was not just at one set but at A, B, and C. Fresh dung was found on most occasions.

On 7 January it snowed slightly and tracks showed up the next day at all sets. On 9 January it snowed again and tracks were found once more. From the 10th to the 19th it was somewhat milder, but on the 20th there was a fall of snow followed by a temperature of 22° F. Tracks were noted the next day at all sets, some of them of different sizes showing that more than one badger had emerged. At A a lot of leaves had been pushed out from three separate entrances on top of the snow and badger tracks were everywhere. That evening there was a further sprinkling of snow, followed by a sharp drop in temperature, but by morning there were signs of intense activity again at all sets. Much more bedding had been ejected at A and some at B. It snowed hard throughout the following night and well into the next day, so no tracks were visible, but on the 24th the tracks showed up plainly, showing where the badgers had romped on a fallen tree, scattering the snow and leaving their fresh claw marks on the bark. That night there was a temperature of 16°F., but signs of activity were abundant the next day at all the sets. About a fortnight later cubs were born at A.

To summarize the points: from 25 December to 25 January there was one of the coldest spells for several years, with only a slight let-up in the middle: if the badgers were going to hibernate they should have done so then. But during the whole period, and often on several successive nights, activity was noted. The activity was not the work of a single restless animal, but occurred at all occupied sets quite regularly. As it was known for certain that there were pairs at each set, and one pair only at each, it follows that this activity was the rule for each badger and not the exceptional activity of a minority.

I have more evidence of this regular activity at mid-winter during other years, but the repeated slight falls of snow during 1944–5 made a check on badger activity so much easier to get that the evidence is more complete. The following year was milder and we had little in the way of snow to make tracks visible. However, there were numerous signs which confirmed the findings of the year before. Several counts were attempted in November 1945, and, although none of these were conclusive as complete counts, owing to the late emergence of some individuals, some badgers were seen each time. On 20 November quite a lot of excavation was noted at A, B, and C. Sticks were put up and by 5.30 p.m. they were already moved at A and C, and by the next morning they were also down at B. The sticks were put up again on 25 November, and again all were down the next morning. On 1 December the holes were all blocked up for a hunt, but by next morning one hole from each set was unblocked. By 5 December these holes were well opened up again at A, B, and C, but there was little evidence of activity at D. On 9 December sticks were again put up and all were down by morning at A, B, and C. Fresh dung was noted in quantity in the pits used by badgers at A and B, showing that they were still actively feeding and moving about freely. On 12 December we watched at all sets, but only saw one badger by 7 p.m., when we left. On 23 December my friend Peter Palmer braved the elements and watched a set at 4.15 a.m. to see what took place. It was a very bright moonlight night, or should I say morning, and at 5 o'clock he saw two badgers come across the field and go down the set he was watching; they had obviously been out on an expedition together.

Towards the end of December the holes were again blocked up for a hunt but once again the entrances were quickly unblocked. On 4 January there were obvious signs of activity at A, B, and C, and fresh dung was noted. I left the district a few days later, but Carus-Wilson, Groves, and Menzies tell me that towards the end of the month the holes were once more blocked up by the hunt and unblocked by the badgers. Pad marks were also noticed on 2 February in the snow.

I made further observations on badger activity during the winter of 1946-7 at one of the large sets on the Quantock Hills in Somerset. Before Christmas the weather was mild, and throughout December and early January activity was regularly noted. Fresh dung was found on each visit, and this was found to contain a very high proportion of grass. On 19 January I found that several holes had been freshly cleaned out. After this we had much snow and the roads were impassable, so it was not until 3 February, after a partial thaw, that I was able to go again. On this occasion tracks were very noticeable in the vicinity of four widely separated holes, because mud had been brought up from the sets on the badgers' feet and been trampled into the snow. More heavy snow followed and extremely low temperatures were recorded but when I was again able to reach the sets on 20 February I found fresh dung and many well-worn paths in the snow.

The lowest temperatures for many years were recorded during January and February 1947 and in many parts it reached zero. James Fisher gave me some extremely interesting facts about the activities of badgers at Ashton, Northamptonshire, on the night of February 24–25. The temperature at 7.30 a.m. on 25 February was –2°F., but in spite of this the badgers had been active. He noticed the tracks of probably four badgers leading from the set in two directions. On following the trails he came upon a place more than a hundred yards away, where they had played in the snow before continuing their travels.

I think I can say that the above evidence proves conclusively that badgers do not hibernate in Southern England. Whether this also applies to the hill badgers of Scotland I do not know: a series of accurate observations would be difficult to make in a mountainous district like that. Mortimer Batten says, however, that many times he has followed their tracks over the snow in these mountainous districts, so hibernation seems unlikely.

Millais (1904) writes that 'in Germany, Sweden and South Prussia badgers may be said to hibernate completely, for in most winters they sleep continuously from November to March'; but he quotes Ekström as saying that 'the winter sleep is not very deep, for, like bats, they will emerge to feed if a long thaw sets in.'

To my mind Millais's statement is too sweeping, as there are many records from Germany of cubs being dug up in February and at least one record for January. I cannot envisage a mammal having cubs during true hibernation, when metabolism is so reduced. It is true that bears have cubs during the winter months, when they are said to be hibernating; but here the term is very loosely used, as it has been established that when bears bed up during cold spells the temperature of their blood does not drop as is the case with true hibernation, and they can easily be roused from their torpor

(Hamilton, 1939). Thus it would appear that in Europe the badger exhibits a transition from no kind of hibernation in the south through partial hibernation in the central region to what approximates to complete hibernation in the coldest regions. Bobrinskii (1944), writing of the badger in Russia, states: 'The rest chamber, in which the badger spends the winter, is lined with dry herbs, leaves and moss; unlike all other Mustelidae the badger hibernates, but its sleep is not sound, and in the south (Transcaucasia, for example) fails to occur at all.'

The following is an abstract from a Russian work by Ognev (1931) concerning the badger in Eastern Europe and Northern Asia: 'The badger spends most of the winter in a passive state, but will go for walks when the temperature rises above freezing, and it emerges when thaw patches appear in the snowy ground. It varies with the region, and in the Caucasus mountains they stay in all or most of the winter. In warm Transcaucasia they probably do not hibernate. There does not seem to be much known about Siberia except that in Ussuri at any rate they leave their burrows on warm days during the winter.'

By saying that they do not hibernate I do not imply that badgers are as active at this season as at any other. This is certainly not the case. They are much more loath to leave their sets, as the nights are long and there is no hurry to hunt for food. If the weather is against them and they are not too hungry, no doubt they will stop in for a night or two; but (it must be remembered) this may also happen at other seasons. Batten says that tame badgers are more sluggish in the winter and sleep a lot, but they can quickly be awakened.

Badgers in the spring certainly weigh less than in the autumn, and dissection shows that much less fat is present at the former season. This suggests that feeding is difficult and stored fat is used up by way of compensation. But the badger in the spring is not a bag of bones, as a bear may be after hibernation; on the contrary, it is in excellent condition and is ready to bear cubs in early February and suckle them.

There is no doubt that the badger is able to go for long

periods without feeding, merely existing on the stored fat inside its body. The most famous case of this is told by Fairfax-Blakeborough (1914), who wrote, 'When the late Tom Green had a string of horses in training at Hambleton, he and his hind one day saw the track of a badger in the snow. This was about Christmas Day, and on following the badger to his home among the rocks they set a trap and walled it in very tight so that Brock had to come out into the trap or, as the only alternative, starve to death inside. For no less a period than fourteen weeks the badger refused to take the trap, but then he abdicated and was taken alive. He was found to be very thin, at which one cannot wonder. Although this well-authenticated case goes to prove that the badger can exist without any further support than he can obtain from his internal supply, it must not be taken that every badger would be in a physical condition to hang on to life for anything like fourteen weeks without food.'

This case, if true (and I see no reason for doubting it), suggests to me that the badger was once a hibernating animal, and that the colder the climate today the more it reverts to the hibernating habits of its past. I do not doubt at all that in parts of Russia and Siberia the badger cannot do anything else but hibernate, as proper food is impossible to get for many weeks on end. In Britain and the more temperate parts of Europe it does not hibernate; but if conditions are temporarily bad it still retains the power to become physiologically sluggish and to go without food for long periods, utilizing the fat stored in its body to keep it alive.

CHAPTER 8

THE MUSK-GLANDS AND THEIR USES

ONE of the characteristics of the family Mustelidae is the possession of musk- or stink-glands. These anal glands vary greatly within the group as regards the potency of the secretion.

The skunk undoubtedly has pride of place in this respect. On being molested or attacked the skunk will turn around, raise its tail, and squirt out a stinking yellow fluid which diffuses such a nauseating smell that the attacker is nearly suffocated. The smell is so persistent that if it gets on a person's clothes no amount of washing will remove it over a period of months.

Weasels and stoats have a less nauseating secretion, but polecats can be extremely unpleasant in this respect, to say the least. In these animals various functions have been assigned to the glands. One is that the oily matter secreted is rubbed on to some piece of vegetation or rock on passing, to indicate to others of the same species that another is about. This presumably is for mating purposes, and the habit seems to be well established for the weasels and martens, which have their regular musking-places. I have never seen badgers behaving in this way, though I have no doubt that the secretion provides the characteristic odour of the badger, which, although slight under normal conditions to us, would give obvious intimation to others of the species of its proximity.

The wolverine is known to foul its food so that no other animal will touch it, and it uses the secretion from these glands to do so. But all observations on the feeding habits of badgers suggest that this is not true for them. I have never known a case myself, nor read of one, where a badger has returned to the same food another night. Normally it never eats anything big enough to warrant this.

Sir Alfred Pease (1898) connected the power of living for long periods without food with the habit of licking the secretion from the musk-glands. He elaborated this unusual theory as follows: 'But there is no doubt that the badger licks this substance, whether by way of taking a tonic, a cooling draught, a stimulant or other physic, I cannot say. I am, however, inclined to believe that from this source he is able to maintain his health and support life during those long periods of seclusion and total retirement in his earth which have led naturalists to describe him as a hibernating animal.'

There is, I think, a much simpler explanation for the presence of these musk-glands under the tail, and I have not seen a badger licking this part of its anatomy more than any other. I am surprised that naturalists who have studied the badger have not come across instances of the glands being used, because I have noticed it on many occasions. Before discussing the functions of the glands it is well to notice the circumstances under which they were used. On a rather dark night in June I was walking quietly down the main ride of Conigre Wood after the badgers had dispersed from their sets. I heard the familiar padding of a badger coming towards me, so I stopped and waited. As the footsteps approached I realized that I had stopped exactly on a badger path crossing the ride. It was too late to move without risk of being heard, so I waited. Soon I could just make it out as it topped the bank and came towards me. It did not discover me until it was about a foot away. Then with a gruff bark of fear or surprise it dashed headlong away, leaving behind it a tremendous smell of badger. Fright had stimulated the glands and the reaction was like the skunk's, but the odour was not really unpleasant – just very strong and musky. I have noted exactly the same reaction on several occasions and it is clear that fright is one cause.

This, however, is not the most usual cause. There are no animals besides man to make the badger really frightened, and it seldom comes across man at such close quarters suddenly. The suddenness of the realization that I was there was the important point. Most of the other occasions on which I have noted the considerable emission of scent have been connected with excitement of various kinds. It can occur at any season of the year; I have even noticed it in late November, but most obviously during June, July, and August. It is at this period that play is at its height, and not in the early spring as stated by Mortimer Batten (1923). In June the cubs and adults play together, and if their excitement increases to a high pitch then the scent is emitted. It is obvious twenty yards away and it hangs about for some time. I remember coming on a set when the air was still rank with it, but no badgers were in sight when I arrived; I had heard them go off previously in a stampede towards their feeding grounds.

The excitement has to be considerable before the scent is emitted. At first they play quietly and no smell is noticeable. This excitement may be of a sexual nature, and on one occasion the scent was emitted during the excited playing just prior to copulation.

I have no doubt that the secretion from the musk-glands in the skunk, the stoat, and the marten is a defence mechanism. In the badger I doubt whether the scent is sufficiently unpleasant to have the same effect, but I think that physiologically it has the same connexion. It may even be mainly vestigial from a functional point of view now that the badger has so few natural enemies. This seems to be extremely likely, as the teledu (*Mydaus*), a very near relative, uses its musk-glands as a defence, and is called the stinking badger for that reason. It is probable that any great emotion may cause its emission, and this would apply to the whole group of musk-bearing mammals. The stimulus may be fear, it may be surprise, it may be excitement in stalking the prey, as in weasels, it may be sexual excitement; the type of response is probably the same in each case.

CHAPTER 9

THE REPRODUCTIVE CYCLE AND ASSOCIATED HABITS

THE reproductive cycle of the badger has long been a mystery to naturalists, and this was the main problem we set out to solve when we started our observations in Conigre Wood. A number of observations had been reported from time to time which seemed to indicate the probable answer to the problem, but much of this evidence was contradictory, and it was necessary to get much more accurate evidence before the whole story could be told with certainty.

There is one fact about which few will disagree, and that is the time when the cubs are born. In the south of England the usual time is February, though births in early March are common. It is, however, subject to a good deal of variation, as January births have been recorded and there are a number of records for April. It would appear that in the north March is the most usual month. The earliest record I have been able to discover was one mentioned by Fischer (1931). This occurred in Germany, when a litter of three cubs was discovered on 19 January; of these two could see but the third was blind. Assuming that they are blind for about nine days after birth, this would bring the date back to 10 January – a remarkably early record. Batten mentions having seen the footprints of badger cubs at the entrance of a set on 15 March in the New Forest. This suggests a January birth, as it is usually considered that a badger will keep her cubs below ground for about eight weeks under normal conditions. This, of course, is somewhat hypothetical, and to my mind eight weeks is a trifle long, but weather conditions must modify the time to some extent.

From data collected on the Continent, the latest known date for cubbing was 14 April. Batten (1923) says that this may occur as late as July but I have been unable to find the actual references (in the *Zoological Record*), and suspect that these late dates may apply to animals kept in captivity. Abnormal conditions such as these may well cause a late birth, as I will make clear later. In the natural state, however, these cubs would only be above ground by September and the winter would be upon them before they were half grown.

One of the chief mysteries about the badger was when it mated. Knowledge on this point would fix the vexed question of the period of gestation. When I started my investigations the position appeared to be as follows. On the Continent the general consensus of opinion was that mating took place in the autumn or late summer, the period ranging between the extremes of July and November, according to different authorities. The position was summarized by Lönnberg (1928), a Swedish authority on the Mammalia, as follows: 'In most faunistic works it is stated that the pairing of the badger takes place in the autumn. Some authors indicate even such a late time as November, while others quote October. ... A German authority, Schäff ... from the beginning of August to the beginning of October. Dr Fritz Schmidt says ... July to August.' Lönnberg himself, however, believed it took place in May.

In this country a similar diversity of opinion existed, the evidence, as on the Continent, being fragmentary and most unsatisfactory. However, the opinions may be grouped into two main categories, those favouring the autumn and those favouring the early spring. The table (next page) makes clear the divergence of views of the more reliable authorities.

From this list it will be seen that most opinion centres round the late summer and autumn, but three modern authorities favour spring. Let us first consider the evidence brought forward for the spring mating.

Mortimer Batten (1923) discusses the matter in some detail. He believes mating takes place almost immediately after the birth of the cubs and that gestation is close on twelve months. He bases this opinion on the following: (1) a number of old records, many of which show gestations of twelve months or more; (2) 'that sexual excitement is at its height

Authority	Year of Publication	Country	Mating time	Gestation
F. H. Salvi	1888	Britain	?	12 months
Sir A. Pease	1898	,,	?	9 months
H. Johnston	?	,,	October	6 months
J. Paterson	1904	,,	July	7 months
Meade-Waldo	1894	,,	October	5 months
Fairfax-Blakeborough	1911	,,	Sept.–Oct.	5–6 months
Millais	1904	,,	Autumn	?
Mortimer Batten	1923	,,	March	12 months
Frances Pitt	1941	,,	Aug.–Oct.	?
Schäff	?	Germany	Aug.–Oct.	7 months
Dr Fritz Schmidt	1934	,,	July–Aug.	7 months
Fischer	1931	,,	August	6 months
Prell	1930	,,	Summer	?
Vogt	1887	,,	Autumn	?
Lönnberg	1928	Sweden	May	10 months
Svantesson	1926	,,	May	10 months

in the early spring, at exactly the same time of year that most of the young are born ... and towards the end of March excitement begins to decrease till by the beginning of June the badger community has settled more or less to its normal mode of existence'; (3) 'at this season badgers are found in pairs more regularly than at any other season, and very often in new and temporary quarters, indication that they are running together'; (4) 'at this season the males are more restless and more often found in out-of-the-way places'; (5) 'that most animals mate again immediately after the birth of their families ... rats, rabbits, hares and the like within a few hours.' Finally he says: 'If seven months were the period of gestation, mating would be in full swing in July, and this certainly is not the case. Moreover, if the many couples found living in solitude together during February and March are not mating, what are they doing? That love matches occur at that season cannot be doubted by anyone.'

First of all, the old records he goes upon are not conclusive. His quotation from F. H. Salvi runs as follows: 'My badger, which had her first family of one (a female) on 27 February last year, presented me with another family on 16 February this year. Naturalists will therefore be glad to know that I can now settle that vexed question, the gestation of these curious animals, for this badger has gone with young a year all but about seventeen days.' This statement makes no mention at all of pairing, and as far as I can see only shows when cubs were born. Then he quotes Vyner as 'saying with certainty that badgers go twelve months with young'. On looking up this reference, I find it is only a second-hand opinion based on the evidence given him by a neighbour who 'some years ago dug out a badger in the spring. She was confined to an outhouse for twelve months, at about which period she produced one young one. During her confinement it was impossible for her to be visited by a male.' If this account is true, it would be good evidence of twelve months' or more gestation.

Secondly, sexual excitement is not, from my observations, at its height in early spring. Having watched badgers many times at this period of the year I would say that at this season there is less play and excitement than at any other with the exception of the winter months, and that, on the contrary, from May onwards the excitement increases – reaching its greatest height in July, August, and September. I watched badgers on eighteen occasions in 1945 between 5 February and 29 March, and only on two occasions can I find any reference in my diary to excitement, although the accounts are full. One of these referred to a brief skirmish between a mated pair on 17 February, and the other to more prolonged playing by three badgers on 27 February. On the other sixteen occasions their behaviour was characterized by quiet exits and lone foragings.

Thirdly, from my experience, *mated* pairs are together practically all the year (see tables of distribution), though yearling badgers, not yet mature and not quite fully grown, are to be found in outlying sets in early spring; these may be cubs from the same parents. I think too that the restlessness of the males at this time of year is true only of those that have lost their mates or are still immature. I would also say that this restlessness is probably more characteristic of a slightly later period.

Fourthly, Batten's analogy with other mammals pairing after the birth of the cubs is not a good one as the majority of animals do not do this, and he quotes rabbits, rats, and hares which have several litters a year in most cases and are not nearly related to the badger. The more nearly related carnivores do not do this.

Lönnberg puts the case for May as the month of mating, 'because of the restlessness and extensive wanderings of males during spring and early summer. Since then proofs have been obtained for the correctness of my views. A trusty gamekeeper, K. Larsson, has told me the following observation of his. An evening in May he was standing watching the flight of woodcock when he saw a badger coming towards him; when it was near enough he shot and killed it. He did not, however, stir from the spot and let the badger lie where it fell. Some short time afterwards he saw another badger coming, eagerly sniffing in the tracks of the first one. This one was also shot and an examination proved that the first one was a female, the second a male, which evidently was following and seeking the female. The strong smell of the animals indicated the rutting season.' I am truly amazed that such material should be submitted as evidence in a reputable scientific journal. If he had ever watched badgers in the wild he would know that at any time of year badgers constantly leave their sets one after the other and follow the same track. I have watched nine do so in succession. Wouldn't any badger sniff at the dead body of another badger found in the path? As for the smell, I feel that it is poor policy to base a theory of pairing on smell when the animal happens to possess musk-glands which it uses all the year round!

Svantesson, quoted by Lönnberg in the same article, gave an account of how, 'in the evening of 27 May 1926 at Liane, in the parish of Dalskog in the province of Dalsland, he saw two badgers playing with each other and witnessed also their pairing.' Lönnberg thus concludes that May is the month. He, however, admits that 'it has been observed that badgers in confinement in the Zoological Gardens "Skansen" in Stockholm have paired in September', but such occurrences, he continues, 'may happen although the actual impregnation has taken place.' In fairness, however, he must admit that this argument could be applied both ways and the pairing at the end of May might be an early sign of awakening sexual instincts, true impregnation not taking place, for instance, until July.

Let us there leave the case for spring as the time of pairing. Early in 1944 I had little evidence of my own but I was much more impressed by the evidence for the autumn, because in 1943 one fact of apparent importance stood out. Counts of the badgers in Conigre during the latter part of the year showed that they seemed to congregate at one set during August, although previously to that they were living as families. For instance, I witnessed nine badgers come out of one set on 3, 6, and 10 August. This was the full population for that year in the wood. During the following winter sets A, B, and C were all occupied, but I had not enough data to say when the separation occurred. My supposition was that they would separate off as mated pairs for the winter, and if I could determine when this segregation occurred it would probably coincide with mating. Then I could concentrate on the few weeks around this date with the hope of seeing pairing. So for 1944 I planned to watch much more frequently to find out when separation occurred, and what was the nature of those segregated, whether mated pairs or unmated.

It was thus with great interest that I saw the first family on 23 April at A, two adults and three cubs. We soon discovered that a second family was using B, but there was only a single cub, a very snub-nosed youngster which looked like a cross between a teddy bear and a panda. I got to know this cub quite well during the season, and photographed it on a number of occasions. By the autumn it seemed quite used to me and my flash bulbs, and would take little notice of my presence. These were the only families, so that it followed that from the previous year's nine badgers, two pairs for certain and possibly three had remained; the rest had departed – we did not know when.

These two families kept fairly separate until 31 July, but then, like the previous year, they all came together and lived in one set. From this date until 16 August they were certainly together, nine of them again. As four of these were this year's cubs it followed that five of them were last year's adults, two pairs and the sow that had lost its mate.

There was some doubt as to whether some separation occurred on 25 August, as I only saw five instead of the usual nine at C, and sticks indicated that A and B were both probably occupied. By 20 September, however, separation had certainly taken place, as there were five at B and some at A. I could not observe C. On 7 October conditions were very difficult as it was very dark, but two badgers were seen at A for certain, two at C and probably two at B, but the second of these was only heard. A little later, however, two were certainly seen at B, so the first count was probably correct. In November two pairs were again noted, including a pair at D where previously there was none; but only one at A and either one or two at B. On 11 December the earths were stopped up for a hunt but A, B, C, and D were all opened during the night showing they were still occupied. By the end of the year, however, only A, B, and C were tenanted, as a fox had taken possession of D. The significance of these figures is best realized by referring to the tables.

It thus seemed likely that there were three pairs present and possibly a single extra badger left in the wood, the others (presumably the cubs) having moved off during late autumn or early winter. If all three pairs had cubs in 1945, it would be proof that the cubs and not the adults had moved off. It was possible that the sow that had lost her mate the previous March had paired off with a fresh male, but that was supposition only.

The drop in numbers after late September suggested that these cubs – as they were afterwards proved to be – went off on their own and left the community for good during October. The activity of the three pairs remaining in the wood during the winter has been described under 'hibernation' in another chapter (p. 101), and a good deal was seen of them during March. The odd badger was seen on 27 February and 1 March, but never again after that. Presumably it was an unattached visitor. Towards the end of March the three pairs were much in evidence, but unfortunately on the 17th one boar from C put its foot in a rabbit trap and was killed the next morning. This event had an interesting sequel as its mate had already had cubs, but that is a later story.

We eagerly awaited the cubs above ground which we expected at A and B, and we hoped for cubs at C but were not sure at that time whether the death of the male might have had some effect. On 5 April I first observed cub droppings at the lavatory used by badgers at A. By bad fortune I had to go away, but on my return I went at once to A and to my delight saw two cubs with the two parents together. Sticks had not been moved at C but I heard badgers at B playing together and assumed that at least two were present.

On 1 May I was able to get help in my watching, and while I was observing the family at A, four cubs were seen at B with three adults; these, as already described, were later found to be two families with two cubs each. One family was the yellow female with her two sandy cubs, and the other a normal couple with two young of usual colouring. As the two sandy cubs were extremely small it is probable that the female at C, after losing her mate, waited just long enough for her cubs to be able to follow her and then decamped to live with the other family at B. As I found later, she returned to her old set, but not until the danger was very much a thing of the past.

We had now good grounds to work on. There had been a segregation of mated pairs in the late autumn, the last year's cubs had departed, probably in October, each pair had produced young, and one family was easily identifiable because of its colour. What would happen next? There were now eleven badgers in the wood including six cubs; this was more than in the previous year.

At this point I must break off the story as an important

DISTRIBUTION OF BADGERS IN CONIGRE WOOD, RENDCOMB, GLOUCESTERSHIRE

(Summary of visits when positive results were obtained)

Date	A	B	C	D	E	Remarks
1944						
April 23	2a 3c	–	–	–	–	
May 8	2a 3c	–	Several	–	1a	
May 20	1a plus	2a 1c	2a	0	0	
May 24	–	2a 1c	Several	–	0	
May 27	–	0	4a 1c	1	1	Family from B to C
June 7	2a 3c	0	3a plus	I	–	
June 21	4a 4c	0	0	–	–	Two families at A
July 25	0	2	4 plus	3	1	
July 31	7 plus	0	0	0	–	
Aug. 8	0	0	9	0	0	All together
Aug. 10	0	0	7 plus	0	0	,, ,,
Aug. 11	0	0	7 plus	0	0	,, ,,
Aug. 13	0	0	7 plus	0	0	,, ,,
Aug. 16	0	0	9	0	0	,, ,,
Aug. 25	–	–	5 plus	0	0	,, ,,
Sept. 1	–	–	Some	–	1	
Sept. 20	Some	5	–	–	1	Partially split up
Oct. 4	Some	Some	2	–	–	
Oct. 7	2	1 plus	2	0	0	

Date	A	B	C	D	E	Remarks
1944						
Oct. 28	-	2	-	-	-	
Oct. 30	Several	Several	2	-	-	In pairs
Nov. 4	1	1 plus	2	2	-	Sets opened after earth stopping
Dec. 10	Occupied	Occupied	Occupied	Occupied	0	
Dec. 24	Occupied	Occupied	Occupied	Occupied	0	
Dec. 30	Occupied	Occupied	Occupied	0	0	Fox now at D
1945						
January	Occupied	Occupied	Occupied	0	0	
Feb. 5	Between 2 & 4	Between 2 & 4	1	-	0	
Feb. 17	Between 2 & 4	Between 2 & 4	2	-	0	
Feb. 20	-	3	2	-	0	
Feb. 27	2	2	2	-	1	
March 8	1 or 2	2	1 or 2	-	1	
March 11	-	-	2	-	-	
March 14	2	-	2	-	1	
March 17	2	2 or 1	2	-	1	Male trapped on morning of March 18
March 20	1	2	1	-	1	
March 23	2	2	1	-	1	
April 3	2	2	-	-	1	
April 5	2	2	1	-	1	
April 26	2a 2c	2 plus	0	0	0	Cubs above ground at A

DISTRIBUTION (continued)

Date	A	B	C	D	E	Remarks
1945						
May 1	2a 2c	3a 4c	–	–	–	Two families at B
May 12	2a 2c	1a 2c	–	–	–	
May 16	Several	2a 2c	–	–	–	
June 6	0	4a 4c	1a 2c	0	0	Two families at B
June 15	–	3a 4c	2a 2c	0	0	Full number again, 11
June 20	–	1a 2c	Many	0	0	
June 23	–	1a 2c	8	0	0	Full number
June 27	2a 2c	2a 2c	1a 2c	0	0	Full number
July 20	–	7 or 8	–	–	1	
July 27	3a 4c	2a 2c	–	–	1	Full number
July 29	3a 4c	Several	–	–	1	
Aug. 1	4a 4c	1a 2c	–	–	1	Full number
Aug. 23	0	0	7 plus	0	0	All at C
Aug. 25	0	0	9 plus	0	0	All at C
Sept. 5	7 plus	0	0	0	0	All at A
Sept. 8	10	0	0	1	0	
Sept. 13	4	0	Several	0	0	
Sept. 22	–	–	7	Some	0	
Sept. 26	0	3	6 plus	0	0	
Oct. 3	2 plus	3 plus	–	–	1	Last time a large count

Date	A	B	C	D	E	Remarks
1945						
Oct. 13	4 to 6	0	0	0	0	Cubs gone
Oct. 19	2 only	0	-	3 or 4	0	
Oct. 22	1 or 2	0	-	3 or 4	0	
Oct. 27	-	1	2	Several	0	
Nov. 1	0	2	1 or 2	Occupied	0	
Nov. 6	4	2	0	0	0	
Nov. 20	Occupied	Occupied	Occupied	Occupied	0	Evidence of sticks
Nov. 21	Occupied	Occupied	Occupied	Possibly	0	,, ,, ,,
Nov. 25	Occupied	Occupied	Occupied	Possibly	0	,, ,, ,,
Dec. 2	Occupied	Occupied	Occupied	0	0	Re-opened after earth-stopping
Dec. 30	Occupied	Occupied	Occupied	0	0	,, ,, ,, ,,
1946						
Feb. 2	Occupied	Occupied	Occupied	0	0	Pad marks in snow
Feb. 21	Occupied	Occupied	Occupied	0	0	Re-opened after earth-stopping

EXPLANATION OF TABLES

The mark – denotes the fact that this set was not watched that night and therefore badgers may or may not have been present. Early in the year cubs could easily be recognized as such and are shown by the letter c as distinguished from adults, a. Later in the season it was not possible to distinguish them with certainty. The term 'plus' suggests that there were indications of others being present, but they were not seen for certain.

event took place. What I expected to happen was this: the badgers would remain as separate families until late July or early August, then be all together for a few weeks – and in September or October I expected to see them mating before separating off for the winter to their respective sets as mated pairs. These expectations were based on the experience of previous years' counts and on the assumption that separation was connected with pairing. Events showed that these expectations were only partly fulfilled. It is true they came together again in August and separated as before in autumn; but my supposition of mating time was incorrect.

I was attempting some photography at the Eycot sets on 14 July; I was up the usual tree with my apparatus all ready. It was very thundery and hot and the badgers started to emerge in good time. Earlier in the season I had counted ten at this set, of which at least four were cubs; on this night at least eight were present. A large boar with a thin white tail emerged first, an animal I could easily recognize. After a few minutes of scratching and waiting he was joined by a rather sleek sow. They sniffed each other but did not play. I was waiting for the others to come out to get a good group when, to my astonishment, the male mounted the female and copulated. There was not the slightest doubt about it being the real thing as it continued for a short time, while I collected my wits, and I photographed them together. The light was very good, and I was only fifteen feet away. It was 10.15 p.m., Double Summer Time.

So they paired in July! And separation in October had, probably, nothing to do with mating! On 21 July three of my helpers, Grant, Hill, and North, were watching the same set; I was elsewhere. They too witnessed copulation, also in good light; this time there was some play previous to pairing, but not very much. Twice in a week seemed to be putting it on a more definite basis. On 29 July I was in Conigre Wood watching at A. I got there at about 9.10 p.m. One family of four came out at 9.25 p.m., the two cubs first, followed by their parents. Almost at once the parents copulated, remaining in position for quite a long time. The boar, on mounting the female, kept her in position by biting her ear, a point I had also noted at Eycot. One cub showed some interest in the proceedings, but was kept at a distance by throaty growls from the boar.

Now this occasion was of significance for several reasons. It not only confirmed the season of mating, but I was here watching a single family, one I had watched all the season. The mother and father were still with their cubs, and they paired again. This proved that one male had the same mate in two successive years and, as they paired when still living as a family, it is strong presumptive evidence that this usually does take place; in other words, they probably pair for life.

It also shows that a female probably has young every year, not every other year as has been suggested. On the next night I was watching this family again and when the adults came out copulation again probably took place but for a shorter period. They certainly took up a mating position, but the light was rather poor and I could not be quite certain that penetration had occurred.

The only other occasion when mating was observed was on 25 August. At this time they were all together at C. There were tremendous chasings and growlings going on for some time at the height of which a male made the 'purring' noise mentioned in a previous chapter and mounted the female. This time, however, the female was unwilling and flattened herself on the ground and after some time the male moved off. During the scuffling, scent was much in evidence.

It would appear from the four or five occasions described that preliminary play is not essential, but it sometimes occurs; but it is certain that at this time of year playing is habitual and reaches its climax. To quote from one entry in my diary for 1 August (two days after witnessing pairing), 'When I got to A at 9.10 p.m., two cubs were already out. Almost at once these were joined by others. There was a tremendous lot of play or fighting. Two adults especially were turning somersaults with each other for minutes on end with great emission of scent. The cubs looked on. The adults came almost to my feet in a swirling furry mass, and then dashed off at full speed. Several others came very near me before hurrying off to C. I then carefully made my way to C and got there undetected. There was much playing again, especially around the poplar tree and the fallen tree. I have seldom seen such sustained scrapping.'

Looking at my diary over several years I note that almost every occasion when this playing has been excessive has been between July and September. It may well be that this play is initiated by the male to excite the female when she is not particularly anxious to pair, but that when she is really ready few preliminaries are necessary.

Since coming to these conclusions I have received more excellent evidence that this is the normal time of mating. Frances Pitt (1945) stated: 'On 13 August 1943 when badger-watching in the early evening in the Caughley Woods, Shropshire, with a badger family playing about me, I saw at a distance of not more than six feet pairing take place between the two adults.' This instance is of great interest as again mating took place when they were still together as a family.

There is also an old but reliable record of mating being witnessed between badgers in captivity by J. Paterson. This is recorded by A. H. Cocks (1903–4). He witnessed an attempt at pairing on 10 July 1898, and a certain pairing on 12 July. One cub was born on 13 February 1899. The next year he only witnessed attempts at pairing but these were also during July. Two further cubs were born on 27 February 1900.

So, collecting all the times when pairing or attempted pairing was seen, we have the data shown in the table on p. 125.

From the above it seems to me conclusive that the normal season of successful copulation is July and early August and that it may possibly extend into September though the sexual urge, at least of the female, may start waning in August.* If,

* Recent observations in the field of research into the reproductive cycle have shown that in addition to the July–September pairings copulation also occur earlier in the year. Fertilization may take place early in the season (February–May), but that does not necessarily prevent further pairings during summer and autumn. – Harrison, R.J., and Neal, E.G., 'Ovulation during delayed implantation and other reproductive phenomena in the Badger.' *Nature*, Vol. 177, pp. 977–9, 26 May 1956.

Date	Authority	Place	Remarks
27 May 1926	O. Svantesson	Sweden	Certain
10 July 1898	J. Paterson	England	Attempt only
12 July 1898	J. Paterson	England	Certain
14 July 1945	E. G. Neal	Glos., Eng.	Certain
21 July 1945	Grant, Hill, North	Glos., Eng.	Certain
29 July 1945	E. G. Neal	Glos., Eng.	Certain
30 July 1945	E. G. Neal	Glos., Eng.	Probably
13 Aug. 1943	Frances Pitt	Salop, Eng.	Certain
25 Aug. 1945	E. G. Neal	Glos., Eng.	Attempt only
September ?	Stockholm Zoo- logical Gardens	Sweden	Certain (?)

then, July is the most frequent time for pairing and February the usual time for cubs, this gives a gestation period of seven months. August pairing would thus give March births; these are of quite common occurrence in the first half of the month. I do not know how to account for the 27 May mating in Sweden, unless (as I have said previously) it was an early sign of awakening sexual instinct, true impregnation not taking place until later. Prell (1930) states in this connexion that bears and certain members of the Mustelidae sometimes exhibit a lesser mating period in spring which seldom leads to reproduction.

To continue with the story of the familes in Conigre: they were all together again, as I expected, after 2 August until 13 September, when there was a partial separation. The next problem was when they would reduce their numbers and whether adults or cubs would move off.

The last time anything like a full count was made was on 26 September, when three were at B and at least six at C. On no occasion after this were we able to count more than six on any one night. So it would appear that separation took place early in October. This confirmed the less reliable evidence of 1944. If they were adults remaining and the cubs had moved off, I expected to find them separating off for the winter in pairs to different sets in the wood, as in 1944, and for each pair to have cubs in the spring.

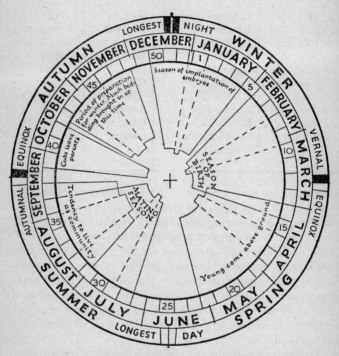

The annual cycle of the badger. Within the period represented by each sector the event marked on it has been observed. Those parts of the sectors enclosed by dotted lines and ending nearest to the centre represent the periods in which the event is most likely, i.e. the peak periods.

They were a long time settling down to their winter quarters compared with the previous year, partly perhaps because the weather was mild (I saw them dragging in leaves in December), and partly because they were upset by having their holes blocked up for hunting on several occasions. The earth-stopping made them very shy, and this made observation more difficult, but it had certain things in its favour. I noticed on each occasion in November, December, and January that the earths were unstopped the night following the closure at A, B, and C; and also at D on one occasion. So separation had certainly occurred. Observations of the animals themselves helped to confirm this.

As I left the district in January I was unable to follow things up myself, but observations were continued by several helpers. I was up again for a few days towards the end of April in the hope of seeing the cubs, but I was a little early and I only saw one cub on one occasion. Observations in May and June, however, showed that there were certainly two families of cubs, and possibly three, but the number was never ascertained finally, as one large group, or, more probably, two smaller ones, were living together and it was difficult to decide which cubs belonged to which parents.

CHAPTER 10

DEVELOPMENT

FROM the evidence cited in the last chapter it seems certain that the gestation period of the badger is about seven months; but how can this be reconciled with the known cases of badgers in captivity when it was a year or even longer? The only way this could be solved was to study the development of the embryo. In any case, I wished to confirm, if possible, by the sizes of embryos in different months, the observations made on mating. It was at this point that I read a paper on badger embryology. It was by a German scientist named Fischer, published in 1931, on the early stages of development. To him must go much credit for doing the basic work.

In order to follow the development more clearly it might be better to outline first of all the usual succession of events in a typical mammal, and then show how the badger differs from it.

Most mammals develop as follows. Ova are formed in the ovaries, and when mature they burst through the follicles of the ovary in which they have developed. Fertilization takes place in various places, such as in the Fallopian tubes, the fimbria, or the uterus, and in some instances even in the abdominal cavity. Meanwhile, as a result of ovulation certain cells within the recently vacated follicles divide to form a temporary ductless gland, the corpus luteum. This organ secretes a hormone into the blood, which, on reaching various organs of the body, stimulates them to prepare for the future welfare of the embryo. One of the first effects of this secretion is to make the uterine wall receptive to the eggs if they have been fertilized. Thus the lining of the uterine wall becomes spongy and the blood circulation develops rapidly in this region. The result is that the eggs, now developed into hollow spheres of cells called blastocysts, embed themselves in the uterine wall and become 'parasitic' on the mother. Various protective membranes are formed round the embryo as it develops; all the oxygen and food it needs is transferred to it from the blood of the mother across a special organ called the placenta. The embryo develops rapidly and regularly up to the time of birth. Meanwhile corpus luteum secretion has been preparing the body for this event, and the mammary glands have developed ready for suckling the young. In most mammals about the size of the badger, the whole development up to the time of birth takes place in two or three months, but the gestation period of a badger is seven months!

Now Fischer found, as in the roe deer, that after fertilization the egg (blastocyst at this stage), instead of becoming implanted in the uterus wall, floated about unattached. Under these conditions, in which food and oxygen were difficult to acquire, the blastocyst's development was slowed up to a remarkable degree, though it did not stop altogether. This stage lasted, according to Fischer, for four months, compared with a few days in most mammals! He then found that the little embryo, now only about 3×4 mm. in size, became implanted in the uterus wall and started to develop at a great pace. Birth took place about seven or eight weeks later.

Fischer was able to measure the size of the blastocysts of quite a number of badgers and, by putting them in the order of the dates when the mothers were killed, he produced a general picture of development. The earliest date on which a blastocyst was found was 30 July, which gives excellent confirmation of our observations of mating. But a mature female on 6 August had none; but the follicles were ripe and ready to extrude the ova. In this ovary there was no corpus luteum. This animal could, then, have taken a successful mating later, in August or possibly in September.

Fischer believes that the four months' period of retarded growth is 'physiologically and inheritably fixed', and therefore the later the fertilization the later the birth. He has shown that implantation usually takes place in early January or late December. Thus on 2 January two females had three blastocysts embedded in each case. One set were very small, about the same size as the non-implanted ones, the others had started to grow quickly and were five millimetres long. Another female on 20 January had two embryos eight millimetres long, and another on 21 January eighteen millimetres. But two badgers he examined, one on 11 January and the other on 29 January, had still got non-implanted blastocysts, and he assumed these were the result of late fertilizations. One female on 3 February showed embryos one hundred millimetres long; these were nearly ready for birth. Further details will be seen in the table which was compiled by Fischer and is reproduced here.

F. L. England tells me of a badger killed in Somerset on Boxing Day with embryos embedded about the size of hazel nuts, suggesting in this case implantation in early December.

Now Fischer estimated that implantation took place four months after fertilization, but I believe this is too short, probably by a month. My conclusion is based on the following data. All the known cases of copulation come between the middle of July and the end of August and are mainly towards the beginning of this period. Similarly, the time of the birth of the cubs ranges normally between early February and the middle of March. This gives a gestation period of seven months. Fischer estimated from his table that, once embedded, the embryo only takes seven or eight weeks to the time it is born. If this time is subtracted from the total gestation period, five and not four months remain. Fischer's estimate was not based on any knowledge of when copulation took place, because at that time it was not known; but, because he found a female with ripe ova on 6 August, he assumed that this was usual and that copulation did not take place normally until August. In the light of our present knowledge this assumption was not justified.

Now we can return to our original query – how can we account for these abnormal cases of more than a year's gestation? The first thing of importance to notice is that they were all of badgers kept in captivity and therefore living under abnormal conditions. The most likely explanation to me is that implantation did not take place at the usual time. In this event it seems probable that the blastocysts would go on living

TABLE OF EMBRYO DEVELOPMENT

From Fischer (1931)

	Date	No.	Size	State of uterus	Experimenter	Place
1	31. 7.1879	2	1·6mm.	Not implanted	Fries	Near Göttingen
2	31. 8.1880	2	1·2mm.	,, ,,	Fries	Near Göttingen
3	16.10.1878	1	1·8×2·5	,, ,,	Fries	Near Göttingen
4	9.11.1899	?	1·8×2·5	,, ,,	Fries	Thuringia
5	10.11.1925	7	1·2mm.	,, ,,	Stieve	Saxony
6	12.11.1925	5	1·2mm.	,, ,,	Stieve	Saxony
7	12.11.1924	3	1·0×1·2	,, ,,	Fischer	Waldkirch,Baden
			1·0×1·4	,, ,,		
			1·2×1·5	,, ,,		
8	12.11.1924	2	1·3×1·5	,, ,,	Fischer	Waldkirch,Baden
			1·0×1·0	,, ,,		
9	22.11.1899	3	1·0×1·2	,, ,,	Fischer	Lenzkirch, Baden
			1·1×1·5	,, ,,		
			1·2×1·7	,, ,,		
10	22.11.1899	4	1·8×1·9	,, ,,	Fischer	Lenzkirch, Baden
			1·1×2·4	,, ,,		
			1·3×2·3	,, ,,		
			1·5×2·8	,, ,,		
11	1.12.1930	1	1·8×2·0	,, ,,	Fischer	Zimmern, Baden
12	16.12.1930	4	2·5×4·0	,, ,,	Fischer	Goppingen, Württemberg
			3·0×4·0	,, ,,		
			2·9×3·9	,, ,,		
			3·1×4·0	,, ,,		
13	29.12.1930	3	2·3×2·3	,, ,,	Fischer	Geisingen, Baden
			2·1×2·1	,, ,,		
			2·0×1·9	,, ,,		
14	2. 1.1901	3	1·5×2·0	Embedded	Fischer	Lenzkirch
15	2. 1.1901	3	5 mm.	,,	Fischer	Lenzkirch
16	11. 1.1931	3	1·4×1·4	NOT embedded	Fischer	Grüsberg, Württemberg
17	20. 1.1921	2	8 mm.	Embedded	Fischer	Eugen, Baden
18	21. 1.1931	2	18 mm.	,,	Fischer	Bachzimmern, Baden
19	29. 1.1931	2	2·0×2·8	NOT embedded	Fischer	Osterburken
			2·0×2·1			
20	3. 2.1925	3	100mm.	Embedded	Fischer	Baden
			AFTER BIRTH			
21	19. 1.1926	3	Two blind, one seeing		Hiller	–
22	7. 3.1862	3	Just born		Herbst	–
23	30. 3. –	–			Nehring	Zoo
24	14. 4. –	–			Hech	Zoo

and growing at a very slow rate until they did eventually become embedded. This would account for the very varied periods of gestation reported over and above the seven months.

Badgers, unless taken as tiny cubs, do not take at all kindly to captivity. They mope and will not feed properly. It seems probable that psychological crisis might easily affect the normal time of implantation, just as in human beings the menstrual cycle may be upset by a psychological upheaval.

It is now possible to state a more fundamental problem of this development. Why is there this period of deferred implantation, and why is it usually terminated after five months? When discussing the problem with my friend Dr L. Harrison Matthews, he suggested that the corpus luteum development might be at the bottom of it, and I agreed that this was the most likely solution.

If this is so I would suggest that after fertilization the corpus luteum does not develop as in most mammals to any extent, but remains small and probably non-secretory until the fourth or fifth month. It then secretes its hormone normally, the uterine wall becomes spongy, and its physical condition makes implantation of the blastocyst inevitable. With adequate food and oxygen now available, the embryo can develop at a normal rate. It is too early to say how probable this hypothesis is, as I am carrying out investigations on it at the moment and material is difficult to get in sufficient quantity to be certain. However, I can say that I examined one female killed on 3 December, in which the blastocysts were not embedded, and subsequently sectioned the ovary. This showed a corpus luteum present, but it was very small. Comparing it with other mammals when the corpus luteum grows rapidly after fertilization, it was very small indeed.

To go still deeper into the problem, we have yet to discover the factor which affects the corpus luteum. Delayed implantation has now been shown to occur in several other animals besides the badger and the roe deer; these include other members of the Mustelidae, the stoat, marten, weasel, and American badger. Dr Matthews tells me there is some evidence that implantation is caused by increased length of day in spring in some cases; this would be recorded by the eye, the stimulus passed to the brain; the brain would affect the pituitary gland, which in turn would probably influence the development of the corpus luteum in the ovary. For the badger it is true that implantation does sometimes occur round about the shortest day, but there are cases of earlier implantation. Also it is difficult to see how day-length could be the factor in an animal which is strictly nocturnal, at any rate at that time of the year. Unfortunately, we shall have to leave the problem there until more is known of the phenomenon.

I would put the average number of cubs born per family as between two and three. Litters from one to five have been reported, but the numbers are easily misinterpreted. For instance, the first badgers I ever watched seemed, to my delight, to be a family of five cubs, but looking back upon it with greater experience I should say it was much more probably two families living together. That five is a possible number I have no doubt, though I have never known a case myself with certainty. Almost all the families I have been quite sure about have been twos and threes, with two cases of a single cub.

Fischer's work has shown that larger numbers are possible. For example, on two occasions four blastocysts were found, and on another seven. But, as Dr Matthews pointed out, it is not unusual in mammals for some of these to be absorbed and never come to anything. This is borne out by the fact that the highest number of embryos Fischer found after implantation was three.

At birth the cubs are about twelve centimetres long, with the tail another three or four centimetres. Usually, if they are not premature, their fur is at first dirty white, the facial stripes not being prominent, but by the time they open their eyes they are much darker and the facial stripes are conspicuous. J. E. Harting (1888), describing cubs born in the Zoological Gardens on 12 March 1862, said: 'They were well covered with short greyish-white hairs and had two dark facial stripes faintly marked.' The largest cub weighed three ounces when born. Two cubs described by A. H. Cocks (1903–4), which were estimated at twenty days old, were nine and three-eighths inches long (the male), and eight and thirteen-sixteenths inches (the female). The black lines were still faint, the upper side light grey and the under side devoid of hair, including the inner side of the legs.

Badger cubs are blind when born, and most evidence points to the fact that they open their eyes after about ten days. Fischer, for example, quotes one case of cubs being found on 19 January by Hiller; two were blind and the third could just see. As this is one of the earliest births recorded, it is unlikely that they would have been long in the blind condition. Cases born in captivity on the whole confirm this, but there are a few exceptions; Patterson (1904), for example, mentions a case of a cub being blind for six weeks; but he remarks that it was completely nude, suggesting a very premature birth.

According to Lönnberg, the badger's tongue is specially adapted for suckling. It is very big, with the lateral margins strongly raised. When the mouth is closed the raised margins of the tongue fit into the palatal furrows and a kind of tube is formed. The young badger grasps one of the teats of the mother and places it in this tube-like space. The strong muscular tongue then alternately squeezes the teat against the palate or gives way, flattening itself in the middle and forcing the milk into the mouth.

The cubs are probably big enough to come to the set entrance after about six to eight weeks, but they are very shy at first and do not wander far. On 28 April 1946, when watching B, I saw what was probably the very first occasion on which a cub was brought above ground. I had watched this set on both 24 and 26 April and had only seen adults. On this occasion the sow came out first after the usual cautious preliminaries and sat by the entrance. She then half disappeared down the set, only to emerge again a few seconds later, followed by the tiniest cub I had ever seen. The cub sat close to its mother on the edge of the set until she got up. It then followed her and crept right under her body. The mother then walked slowly forward with the cub protected and almost completely hidden by her body. When they had approached to within a few yards of where I was watching, the cub came out and scampered back to the set and disappeared. I do not think it was at all likely that it was being suckled, as its position in relation to the mother made this wellnigh impossible. I did not see the cub again; no doubt it had had enough for one evening.

I also watched one family very newly above ground in late April the previous year. The sow emerged first to see if all was well, then, returning to the entrance, she looked down and was met by a little enquiring snout. The little cub eagerly came out, followed almost at once by a second. They kept very near their mother, often touching and rubbing against her, while she kept nosing them. Play was not a prominent feature at first, but they did romp together later, and several times they climbed on top of her. She would lie half over the set entrance and let them clamber over her. One cub started to shuffle leaves in, an instinctive action probably. The cubs were never far from the hole and once, when danger was suspected, the mother yelped and pushed the cubs down in front of her.

When about eleven weeks old cubs are more active and independent. They are often the first to appear at the set entrance, but at this stage they seldom come right out before their parents. They play with each other much more now, and on warm evenings their high-pitched yelps of impatience can be heard some time before they emerge. They are extremely sensitive to noises at this period of development; the moo of a cow or the thumping of a rabbit may send them in at once with a mad rush. A few weeks later they are often seen away from their parents, possibly emerging first to have a preliminary scamper before the adults appear.

I have previously submitted evidence that the cubs leave their parents in October. This was based on a drop in numbers in Conigre during this month. It was shown to be the cubs that had gone and not adults as those that remained all had cubs the following spring. This occurred both in 1945 and 1946. It was of considerable interest when sets were discovered for the first time in November 1945 in a small wood near the school, known as the Upper Wilderness. Badgers had not been there in previous years and enquiries among the boys showed that the new holes were almost certainly excavated during September or October. As they were obviously occupied, it was important to find out if they were paired adults or cubs which had left their parental sets in October. The sets were therefore watched on several occasions, including the summer of 1946, and only two badgers were seen on each occasion; and no cubs were born in the spring (Humphris and Margetts). It was possible, therefore, that these were two cubs from Conigre, as this was the nearest wood to the Upper Wilderness.

Cubs are not mature during their first year (Chelmers Mitchell, 1912). This fact has been endorsed by the behaviour of the young at mating time; as noted before, the parents paired while the cubs were still part-grown and when still living as a family. I presume the cubs mate the following July, when they would be about seventeen months old.

I have also a piece of exact evidence regarding a badger at Wiveliscombe, Somerset. On 26 December 1945 some badger diggers dug out a badger cub aged about ten months. It was a female, so they marked her ear and put her back, although the parents were killed. They were digging again on 25 May 1947 at the same set and caught her again, this time with her two cubs aged about four months. Thus the mother was born in the early part of 1945, mated in her second year, and had her first cubs early in the following year. This instance also suggests that if there is room available in a community, the female cubs may remain and not leave in September or October which appears to be the usual custom of cubs.

THE ANNUAL CYCLE OF BEHAVIOUR

IT is now possible to summarize our present knowledge of the annual cycle of behaviour of the badger, and for this purpose I propose dividing it up into sections, some of which are fairly distinct in nature but which on the whole tend to merge into one another imperceptibly. They may vary a week or so either way, according to local conditions. These sections may be drawn up as follows:

(1) From late January to the end of March. The period preceding and following the birth of the cubs until they first appear above ground.

(2) From April to the beginning of July. The period of cub play and learning and parental care.

(3) From July to mid-September. The mating period.

(4) From mid-September to mid-November. The period of preparation for winter, including the departure of the cubs.

(5) From November to late January. The winter period of reduced activity.

From Late January to the End of March

Early on, their movements are not regular. They come out when they feel like it rather than as a result of conditions such as temperature and light intensity. It is true, however, that warm nights will probably bring them out earlier and bright moonlight nights keep them in later.

The adults are normally in pairs at this season, one, two, or even three pairs in a set. They tend to be in the larger and older sets while the cubs, now nearly full-grown, are mainly in the newer outlying sets.

The behaviour of the adults is somewhat furtive round

about the period of birth, the sow especially being supersensitive to any unusual stimulus. The boar usually emerges before the sow, and often leaves before the latter comes out. He may be away some time, but the sow usually returns within twenty minutes and does not reappear for some time.

There is very little play, though a few scuffles have been noted; on one occasion the excitement was sufficient for the emission of scent, but this was an unusual incident.

Round about the period of birth, the boar is still living with the sow, though I think it probable that he may be in a different part of the set. On two occasions I have noticed the male at this time stand outside the entrance used by the female and make his 'purring' noise by way of calling her, but he would not go in and find her. There is, however, no question of the male being banished completely by the female at this time.

After the cubs are born the difference in behaviour of male and female is well marked. The male is out quite a lot, but the female does not leave her cubs for long periods.

Various excavations occur at this time, first in preparation for the cubs from mid-January into February, and later, in March, after they have been born a short time. Fresh bedding is brought in to replace the old. Towards the end of March there is a good deal of activity and their mergence is more regular.

From April to the Beginning of July

This period begins when the cubs are allowed above ground. At first these outings are not regular and depend largely on the mildness of the weather. The cubs remain near the set entrance and their play is not very energetic. They keep close to their mother and are quick to bolt when danger threatens. They normally live for the first little while in the set where they were born and where the adults spent the winter, but after about a month, or before that under exceptional circumstances, they move off to another set.

The sow pays a good deal of attention to the cubs at first.

She precedes them out of the set. She licks them and searches their fur for parasites. Much of their play is with her. By June, however, the cubs are bolder and more independent and the sow is more carefree. There is much playing at this stage and it is of a much more violent nature than in April or May.

The cubs practise many of the actions that will be of benefit to them later. They drag in leaves during an interlude of play, or start digging holes. During late June or early July it is not at all unusual to find single holes newly dug not far from the main sets. These are never occupied during the day but are visited after dark. I believe they are dug by cubs. Usually they are closed by the earth-stopper and may never be used again, though it is possible that they may be further developed by the cubs prior to leaving their parental sets in the autumn.

This period is one of education. The cubs begin to associate sounds and smells with danger, learn the countryside around their home, and become familiar with the methods of finding different kinds of food. They do not go far from the set without their parents, and at this stage they keep together as a family while they feed.

By July the cubs are not much smaller than their parents though they probably do not reach full size until the following spring or summer.

From July to Mid-September

This is the mating period, with sexual excitement most evident from the end of July, through August and into September. For the first few weeks of this period the badgers are living as families still, but after mating has been successfully accomplished, it would appear from those in Conigre Wood that they tend to live all together for a few weeks. Whether this occurs in all districts and what is its significance, I cannot say for certain, though it may well mean that the other sets are left without occupants for sufficient time to be well aired and cleaned. As noted previously, while living together they often go to their old sets and scour them out very thoroughly. Conigre Wood, however, may well be exceptional in having so many sets, and what happens there so markedly may be less obvious when the sets are more isolated. But it is well known that in most badger districts the sets are not always occupied, and that there is often a seasonal movement from one set to another round about this time.

Their excitement is considerable during this period, with great chasings, scufflings, and mad rushes. Emission of scent is usual and yelping is often heard.

Mid-September to Early November

This is the period when badgers prepare for the winter. By the middle of October the cubs probably leave their parents for good, although before this they may have been preparing their own sets ready for habitation. The parents then set to in earnest and drag in bedding to line their winter quarters. Nights are chosen for this when the material is fairly dry. This continues spasmodically until the end of November.

The pairs separate off towards the end of this period, though it is sometimes the case that a pair will not finally settle down for the winter until December. They settle in the homes they are going to occupy until after the cubs are born.

There is not much excitement or play during these months, especially in November. Their emergence each evening becomes less regular and more dependent upon inclination but they come out on practically every night.

From Early November to the End of January

These winter months are the quietest of the year for the badgers. They come out on any good night, but are in no hurry to do so. Under very adverse conditions they may stay below for two or three days at a time, but this is not usual, and there is no period of true hibernation.

Feeding is more difficult at this season, and although anything discovered is eaten, and in mild weather this may be ample, they depend to some extent on the fat stored in their bodies when conditions are hard, such as during prolonged frost.

By mid-January they are beginning to prepare for the cubs, and the first spring-cleaning of the year takes place.

It might be of interest to add to this summary the diary of a single family over the period when its identity was certain; the family with the bright sandy-yellow mother.

On 12 October 1944 the pair made their winter quarters at C, no others being with them at this set. They lived there continuously until the two sandy cubs were born, probably towards the end of February. On 17 March the boar was trapped, but the cubs were too small to move. On 11 April the sow took her two cubs, still very small and unusually young for such a trip, to B, where they lived with a second family. I am not certain how long they were at B, but by 6 June the sow had taken her cubs back to C, her original home. By 15 June they were back at B again, this time alone, as the other family had gone in the meantime to A. On 27 June they were back again at C, where they remained for about a month before living with another family for a few days at A. At some time in August they again moved off to C, where they lived together with all the other badgers in Conigre. Their further fate was not possible to observe as the light in autumn and winter, at the time when they emerge, is insufficient to detect colour differences.

CHAPTER 12

BADGER SETS AND LIFE UNDERGROUND

How often have I wished that glass roofs could be inserted over the badger tunnels and electric light laid on for the observation of their activities underground! What happens in the darkness of the maze of tunnels will probably remain much of a mystery, but some light has been shed on the subject through the exertions of the badger-digger.

Just as a fox's burrow is called an earth, so a badger's is called a set or sett, whichever you will. Sets are to be found most often in hilly districts, especially if these are well wooded. In places where badgers are common they have spread to less typical habitats. The mountain badgers live, of course, in places where trees are less abundant and often absent, and their whole life is somewhat different because of their more barren surroundings.

The site chosen is often within a short distance from water, well-worn tracks telling of the badgers' habitual excursions for a drink. Sometimes the sets are actually tunnelled into the bank of streams, but they are always well above the water line. This is true of two sets I know in Gloucestershire.

In the south and west it is in the copses and small woods where sets are most frequent, especially if the copses are on a slope. Gwion Davies (1936) examined twenty occupied sets near Denbigh, all of which were in slopes or banks, seventeen being in woods. In my experience of the south-west of England I can only recollect one set of any size not in the vicinity of trees, though I have known them in hedgerows in which a number of small elms were growing.

Ritson Graham describes the haunts of the badger in Lakeland as follows: 'Many, probably the majority, of the earths I have examined are situated on the banks of streams, and in this general statement I include every kind of water-worn defile, from the narrow ravine to the wide river valley, a particular type of physical feature abounding in Cumberland ... The position of the set in the broad valley or the narrow gill is as varied as the site itself; it may be almost at water level or on the brink of the bank, at the head of the water that feeds the gill or down by the broad sweep of the river. The majority of these valley earths are sheltered and more or less concealed by trees or bushes; exceptionally they are in the open, though this is often due to subsequent felling of the trees or clearing the brushwood. The next most common type of haunt is the tree, scrub or bracken-covered slope.' He goes on to say, 'There are many badger haunts in comparatively open country, and many earths in treeless localities. As examples of treeless or otherwise exceptional sites, we find badgers established in abandoned quarries and old coal drifts, in thick hedgerows and disused sand pits, and in bare hill sides. Thus, while the bank is preferred and some cover desirable, the badger is adaptable and can secure a home in almost any kind of country. A feature of the badger's haunt is the evident desire of the owner for peace, the earth being invariably situated in a quiet place though not necessarily far removed from human habitation.'

Badgers will dig into most soils, clay or sand, according to the district. Sandy soil is easier for them, and the largest deposits of earth outside set entrances are found where the soil is light. In the Cotswolds the badgers frequently choose pockets of clay which are often to be found between the more typical areas of limestone rock. Gwion Davies states that, of the Denbigh sets, ten were in clay and six in sand. In Somerset several soils are utilized. In the Blackdown Hills the largest sets follow a line just below the escarpment on the north side and are found in the Greensand. In the Quantocks the badgers burrow into the shaly banks, and in other parts they make good use of the red sandstone. I have visited several sets where tremendous excavations have been made at the base of red sandstone cliffs, and it was interesting to see how the reddish deposits of sand from their paws passed up a sloping tree outside one set to a height of about twelve feet from the ground.

All sorts of woods and copses are chosen, but with old sets

the types of trees growing in the immediate neighbourhood are often determined by the activities of the badgers themselves. The great deposits of earth constantly voided from the sets, and the innumerable entrances made over long periods of time allow only certain types of plants and tree seedlings to survive. This, together with their habit of feeding on the more succulent and palatable plants, results in a fairly typical flora of nettles and elders near the sets. If the sets are more recent, the original forest or copse trees may persist. In moorland, conditions are different.

I know of one locality on the Quantocks where the holes occupy an area of woodland approximately an acre in extent. The soil is soft shale and their tunnels are everywhere. The set goes back many hundreds of years and has the reputation of being one of the larger ones in Somerset. The whole of this area is a mass of elders and nettles, except at the extreme end, where there are no badgers and where a few of the great forest trees still remain.

Another set in the Blackdown Hills is of great size and covers an immense area. More than fifty holes were counted, although the majority of these were not regularly used. J. G. Millais (1904) describes a set in Staffordshire where forty-four openings to the galleries were in view at one time.

It must not be assumed, however, that in these tremendous sets there will be a comparable number of badgers. I have spent many evenings watching the large sets in Somerset and I have been surprised and disappointed at the small number of badgers seen or heard compared with the number of entrances. Of course, watching is more difficult, for when you are right for the wind for one entrance you may be wrong for others, so you may not see all that are there. However, I think the true explanation is largely in terms of available food, and the fact that these places are seldom disturbed by man and earth-stopping is too difficult a task. So the old sets remain open and the badgers keep making new ones. Further evidence that the numbers in some of these big sets is relatively small is the fact that comparatively little dung is found near them. If many animals were there, enormous deposits would be found! Howard Lancum, from his experience of large sets in Devon, endorses this view.

The number of entrances is therefore not always an indication of size though the development of a set over a number of years may be indicated by the number of new entrances pushed out. In Conigre Wood, in spite of the activities of the earthstopper, we were able to get some indication of this development by counting the holes each August before earth-stopping had eliminated any of them. The following table shows the results obtained:

Set	Year started	Number of holes per set								
		1937	1938	1939	1940	1941	1942	1943	1944	1945
A	1924 (?)	2	2	2	2	3	4	4	5	5
B	1938	–	1	1	2	2	2	3	3	3
C	Ancient	3	3	3	3	4	4	4	4	5
D	1939	–	–	1	1	1	2	2	3	2
E	1943	–	–	–	–	–	–	1	1	1
Total:		5	6	7	8	10	12	14	16	16

As most of this development took place during the war years, when earth-stopping was unusual, it may not be an accurate picture of what usually occurs during more normal times.

New entrances certainly occur when a tunnel comes rather near the surface and the roof falls in. This accident is exploited and turned into a new entrance. This happened very obviously at C in 1944. Air holes of much smaller diameter are often pushed out for ventilation, and these, if enlarged, sometimes become proper entrances. In sets with many holes, it is usual for one to be used by the family in the spring in preference to the others, and it is common for this to be a different entrance each year. The other holes are used as emergency exits, but later in the season, when the cubs are more active, several holes are used and it becomes increasingly difficult to forecast which ones they will use.

On the subject of ventilation holes: I was trying to photograph badgers on one occasion, and had set up my apparatus, when I saw with interest about a yard away some leaves moving. I thought some large beetle or mouse was moving them, but no, there was a quick snort and I heard a badger pound away along the tunnel below me. Presumably it had poked its nose up to sniff the air and had scented me!

Badgers have no exact plan for their underground fortress, but there seems to be a very general one which becomes modified according to individual inclination and soil conditions. Some of the main entrances always lead back a yard or so to a large chamber. Its floor is hardened and smoothed by the feet of generations of badgers. It may be quite spacious and two or more feet high. This probably represents the first breeding chamber long ago when the set was first dug out. From this various tunnels radiate, and these lead to other chambers used as sleeping places or for breeding. It is astonishing how much bedding may be found in some of these. More tunnels lead out of these in a big set and probably go on doing so for a long way. In some soils which are deep and where the sets are dug into hillsides there may be tunnels at different levels. I know of at least one in Somerset where there are certainly three storeys.

The tunnels go in a tremendous way on occasions. I. Thorn, a gamekeeper, was telling me how he was putting in stakes for a fence along a wood near Marsden (near Rendcomb, Glos.). He and his companion were making the holes with an iron crowbar. All went well at first, but then the crowbar suddenly went right in. They found they had driven it into a badger chamber which was found to be more than sixty yards from the nearest exit. Arthur Thompson (1931) tells of a set in the Cotswolds where a terrier was sent in, but did not return. Much later it emerged on the other side of the hill from another badger set a hundred yards away.

No doubt these tunnels are not entirely the work of badgers, as they exploit natural cracks in the rock. In mountainous districts they run largely between great boulders and are not excavated much by the badgers themselves, as there is little need, except, of course, by way of tidying up.

The breeding chambers are often situated in specially well-protected places; a common spot chosen is under the roots of a tree or some large stone or boulder. The badgers will then remove some of the earth from above the roots or stone, and on this platform one of the adults will lie with its face towards the entrance. It is thus in an almost impregnable position and can drop on any intruder. A variation of this method for a similar purpose is for a step to be constructed in the tunnel just below the breeding chamber, so that anything entering is below the badger and would have to leap up the step. An added advantage of this type of construction would probably be good drainage.

Other animals may live in the same set as badgers. Rabbits are often numerous; they make good use of the soft earth thrown out at intervals by the badgers, and make side tunnels of smaller diameter down which a badger could not follow.

Foxes are common inmates, and in large sets a vixen may cub there at the same time as, but in a different part from, a badger family. Foxes are probably tolerated but disliked, and if one is available the badger will probably move off temporarily to another set, especially if the first earth is small. On occasions the badger may eject the foxes. Rats may also be seen emerging from a set entrance at dusk.

This book is in no way a book on sport, but brief reference should be made to badger-digging and -baiting. Sir Alfred Pease (1895) deals with this aspect extremely well, and I refer the reader to him for greater detail. Another booklet, by H. H. King (1931), is also a useful reference book.

When I was first asked if I would like to go to a badger-digging I was asked if I were squeamish, because it was said, 'the end is not always very pleasant.' That is an apt reflection on certain kinds of badger-digging. It would not, however, be at all fair to leave it at that, because there is another side to the business where the cruelty of certain methods is carefully avoided. This is true of the majority of badger-digging clubs which make as their purpose the transferring of live badgers from places where they are getting too numerous to those where they are few.

The normal procedure is to find a set which is known to be occupied (the smaller the better) and to send in a terrier. The dog is trained to find the badger but to keep at a distance. If it approaches too near it may get badly mauled and possibly killed. Its job is to prevent the badger from digging away, a thing it will do as quickly as the diggers the other end if it gets the chance! If the badger turns to dig, the terrier leaps on it and gives it a nip; this makes the badger turn again and the terrier retreats. This is continued for some hours, while the diggers excavate the tunnels in the direction of the yelps made by the terrier. When close enough badger tongs are used to drag out the badger, which is then dispatched by a blow on the nose or put in a sack and transferred alive to another district and released.

Badger-baiting, in its original sense, is probably a thing of the past, but a slightly more humane variation of it still exists to some extent in the larger towns and cities as well as in the remoter country districts. A badger is caught alive and placed in a barrel or box to which it is chained, and the locals bring their dogs to test them out on it. Betting is a usual sideline, and the owner of the badger often makes quite a haul from the owners of inexperienced dogs. The terriers are often badly mauled in the process and even killed, and the badger may suffer a lot of ill-treatment. At one time the badger's lower jaw was cut away to give the dogs more chance. There is nothing whatever to be said for badger-baiting.

Badgers come in for a lot of persecution from all sorts of people; trapping is extensive and some of the less enlightened hunts destroy them whenever possible in spite of the excellent evidence that foxes benefit from the presence of badgers. There are, however, some very notable exceptions and some hunts realize their usefulness and leave them alone.

The Ministry of Agriculture officially classifies badgers as useful animals, but unfortunately this has not prevented the large-scale use of cyanide gas to exterminate them in their sets. In some counties this has been carried out under the auspices of pest control officers, who should be in a position to know better.

If an animal causes harm there is a logical reason for destroying it; but when it is well proved that the good it does far outweighs the occasional harm, why do we go on persecuting it? We are truly an illogical race! We know all about the depredations of the fox; we know it for the rascal it is; but because we like hunting we preserve it carefully, and if we shoot one in exasperation we carefully keep the knowledge to ourselves.

Ignorance about the badger is, on the contrary, appalling. Few people have ever seen one alive, though they may have lived in a district where they are common. They inconsequentially assume they do harm, and when the chance comes they destroy the badgers. The majority of farmers and gamekeepers think and behave in this way, and when the word goes round that there are badgers in such and such a place there is soon a willing gang to help dig them out and kill them. Only the other day I was sent a newspaper cutting about a badger on one of the large estates in Buckinghamshire, which 'had defied all attempts to trap him for fourteen years.' Another newspaper report accompanied by three large photographs told of a recent badger dig on the Mendips which 'provided an exciting time for a dozen or so folk.' The bag in this case was three adult badgers and a tiny cub. All were brought home in triumph. Unfortunately, these are typical examples of the general attitude towards the badger.

It is to be hoped that as people come to know more about these grand animals they will revise their opinions, based on stupidity and ignorance, and begin to appreciate the presence of one of the finest animals on our fauna list.

CHAPTER 13

THE BADGER IN FOLK-LORE
AND FABLE

THE name badger is probably derived from the French word *bêcheur*, a digger (Harting, 1888). This seems a very likely explanation, and no name could be more apt. The name, however, has not been in general use for very long in most parts of the British Isles, because up to the middle of the eighteenth century the names of 'brock', 'pate', 'grey', and 'bawson' were more commonly used. The name 'brock' still persists widely, and is probably of Scandinavian origin. The Danish for badger is *brok*; as also is the Irish Gaelic; the Scottish Gaelic name is *brochlach*. The Welsh normally speak of it as *brock*.

The name 'brock' has given rise to many place names in England such as Brockenhurst, Brockhampton, and Brockworth; but it is in the farm and field names that Brock figures so largely. Ritson Graham writes in this connexion about the Lake District, 'The familiar place-name of *brock* alone ranges the country from the lower reaches of the River Eden to a number of crags extending up to two thousand feet in altitude in the Lakeland fells, whilst the many farm, field and fell names of which Brocklewath, Brockholes, Brocklands and Brocklebank are typical examples, all testify to the prevalence and wide distribution of the badger in former times.'

As Sir Alfred Pease (1895) points out, the expression 'sweating like a brock' is misleading, as in this case it refers to the 'cuckoo spit' insect (the larva of a froghopper) and not to the badger at all.

Harting (1888) suggests that the name 'bawson' has the same meaning as bawsened, which means striped with white. The name 'pate' appears to be more of a local name; it was in common use in the north of England. In Durham there is a small glen called 'Pate-Priest's Glen' after a refugee priest who came over from France and lived a hermit life in the glen and was much given to badger-hunting. The name is also to be found commonly in the parish registers of some of the Lakeland towns in connexion with the paying of head-money for badgers. For example, in the Penrith Parish accounts for 1658 there is an inventory, 'Payed for killing of two Paytes, 2s.' Ritson Graham comments on this paying of head-money for badgers in Lakeland as follows: 'With unremitting zeal this paid persecution of the badger prevailed in the hill parishes of the three counties for almost a hundred years, the first payment recorded being the one from Penrith dated 1658, and the last from Ulverston in 1741. During this period the payment varied from a shilling to sixpence a head, and in a few instances to fourpence. The parishes of Penrith, Kendal, Dacre, Barton, Kirkby Lonsdale, Orton and Ulverston are all mentioned as having paid head-money for the killing of badgers, and Kendal heads the list with seventy-three badgers paid for within a period of eight years.'

The name 'grey' obviously refers to the colour of the animal, and it must have been in common use in olden times as 'There is an act of Elizabeth providing payment for the heads of foxes and grays' (Hyde Parker, 1941).

Another local name is 'badget'; this is probably confined to Norfolk. In Southern Ireland the badger is referred to as the 'earth dog', and in China as the 'sweet-potato pig'.

On the Continent the badger has come in for much more notice than in this country, and it takes an important place in the folk-lore of Germany. To quote from Vogt (1887), 'In fable the badger plays the role of a peace-loving, gentle and cautious Philistine who loves beyond everything his comfort, his family and his home, but who may become furious if alarmed or disturbed in his habits. He is the cousin and friend of the fox, whom he vainly tries to lead back to the path of virtue, but whose defence he undertakes as a good-natured relative in spite of all the malicious tricks that Reynard plays him.' As Vogt remarks, 'With the exception of this friendship, which can scarcely be said to exist, the leading traits in the character of the badger are summed up with great ingenuity in these fables.'

One of the strange statements handed down about the badger in England is that its legs are shorter on one side than the other – an adaptation to walking along hillsides, but presumably rather a nuisance on the home journey! Macaulay referred to this when he wrote, 'I think Titus Oates was as uneven as a badger.'

Some of the most interesting pieces of folk-lore about the badger were collected by Fairfax-Blakeborough (1911). He quotes a manuscript compiled by David Naitby about 1800:

> Should one hear a badger call,
> And then an ullot [owl] cry,
> Make thy peace with God, good soul,
> For shortly thou shalt die.

Also from the fly-leaf 'of Mistress Braithwaite's well-thumbed copy of Holy Writ':

> Should a badger cross the path
> Which thou hast taken, then
> Good luck is thine, so it be said
> Beyond the luck of men.
>
> But if it cross in front of thee,
> Beyond where thou shalt tread,
> And if by chance doth turn the mould,
> Thou art numbered with the dead.

Also from David Naitby's collection comes the following:

A tuft of hair gotten from the head of a full-grown Brock is powerful to ward off all manner of witchcraft; these must be worn in a little bag made of cat's skin – a black cat – and tied about the neck when the moon be not more than seven days old, and under that aspect when the planet Jupiter be mid-heaven at midnight.

As a cure for most ailments the badger cannot be beaten. For example, the *Sporting Magazine* for 1810 states, 'The flesh, blood and grease of the badger are very useful for oils, ointments, salves and powders, for shortness of breath, the cough of the lungs, for the stone, sprained sinews, collachs etc. The skin being well-dressed is very warm and comfortable for ancient people who are troubled with paralytic disorders.'

The merits of badger grease are upheld by many an old countryman. I remember talking to an old rabbit-trapper who regularly trapped badgers to get grease for his rheumatism. He was expounding its virtues and, with a look that seemed to say, 'You dare to say this is not true', he said, 'Badger grease is so penetrating that if you rub it on the palm of the hand, within two minutes you will see it at the back!'

Hyde Parker quotes a Cotswold worthy as saying, 'There's nothing like badger's fat for curing the rheumatism – aye, and most anything else you can think on. It's so strong that if you put a lump on your chest, your hair'd stand on end!' A countryman told A. L. Hendy that badger grease was 'an unfailing remedy for cold in a cow's udder.'

Up to the time of the war, an old villager near Cheltenham regularly prepared badger grease and sold it without difficulty to people who would come long distances to get it. Several people I know are convinced of its usefulness in cases of strains and sprains and use it regularly on horses and other animals. In fact, in most districts where badgers are plentiful there are some people who uphold its merits.

Sidney Lane told me a nice story of how an old worthy in his employ told him one day how he was 'plagued by all that badger lice'. When asked what badger lice was, he was unable to explain, but said he would show him. On reaching the spot he found a tangled mass of cleavers or goosegrass! Apparently the term 'badger lice' is a back-handed compliment to the badger, notoriously very clean, the idea presumably being that cleavers was the only thing that would cling to the animal.

One of the earliest references to the use of badger's skin is in the Old Testament. The precise directions given for the construction of the tabernacle included a covering of rams' skins dyed red, and a covering above of badgers' skins. (Exodus xxvi, 14.) Further, when the tabernacle was to be moved, all the instruments of ritual and the altar itself were to be covered with a cloth of blue and a covering of badger skins. It would appear, therefore, that badgers were not uncommon in Palestine in those days. The skins were also used for footwear by the Israelites, and Ezekiel (xvi, 10) uses the phrase 'clothed in fine linen and shod with badgers' skins' to denote special prosperity.

To-day the skins are not used much except for an occasional rug, but the hairs are extensively used for the best shaving brushes. It is interesting to note in this connexion that the French have one word *blaireau* for both badger and shaving brush. Badger fur is used in Scotland for making the best sporrans, and the term *brochan* was used for the man who trapped the badgers for that purpose. Mortimer Batten tells me that 'in Glen Garry the old brochan still maintains and is proud of his title; in the last few years they averaged twenty-six badgers per season for sporrans.'

Badger hams were at one time smoked and thought much of in England, Wales, and Ireland, but little use is made of the flesh to-day. Dr Hodge tells me, however, that at West Chinnock, near Yeovil, they still have an annual badger feast.

CHAPTER 14

PHOTOGRAPHING THE BADGER

ALL my photographs in this book have been taken with a folding camera, with a ground-glass focusing screen and a f/4.5 Tessar lens of focal length 10.5 cm. Most good cameras can be used for night photography, and some have considerable advantages over the camera I have used. The increased depth of focus afforded by miniature types makes it much simpler, but the photographer has not always a choice in these matters and he must use what he has got.

I use the fastest panchromatic plates or films and stop down as far as possible to increase the depth of focus and improve definition. Using the large type of flash bulb I find it possible to stop down to f/11 at a distance of ten or twelve feet when using plates such as Kodak P 1500. The best flash bulbs for the purpose are those giving a short flash of approximately one-seventy-fifth of a second, unless you have a speed gun to synchronize the exposure with the flash when the long-flash bulbs may be preferable.

I first tried fixing these bulbs into cycle-lamp holders, but found them unsatisfactory as the contacts are so poor. Later I constructed a small wooden box to hold the cycle-lamp battery and fixed to it a reflector similar to those used for indoor work with photoflood bulbs. A short flex led from the battery to a bell-push switch.

This apparatus could be used in two ways. First it could be clamped to the base of the camera, so that whichever way the camera pointed the flash bulb did so too. The two pieces, camera and flash apparatus, could then be attached to the same tripod, making it easy to set up at a moment's notice. The other way was to hang the flash apparatus independently of the camera on to anything handy.

Although the former method had many advantages, I prefer the latter on the whole. I found that with the first method

I was more liable to catch the reflection of the light in the eyes of the badger as camera and bulb were too near together. A further disadvantage was the weight of the combined apparatus which proved rather too much for the smooth working of the universal head on the top of the tripod. It had the great advantage, however, of leaving both hands free, one for the cable release to the shutter and the other for the flash-bulb switch.

Focusing is always one of the greatest difficulties when you have very little depth of focus; of course you cannot do it in the dark. I found it necessary to focus carefully in the day-time and note the reading on the scale for future reference. This meant knowing the exact places where the badgers were likely to be that night. This is really the most difficult part of badger photography by a long way. The photographic technique can soon be learnt, but knowledge of the animals themselves is essential before you can get good photographs.

At first I found it very difficult to approach near enough to get good detail, and it was several years before I knew the animals sufficiently well to get good close-ups. Eventually, however, I found it possible on occasions to get within seven feet of single badgers and photograph them successfully.

To make the focusing easier, I marked out the two or three possible vantage points round each set in Conigre Wood and learnt the focusing distances to the places where the badgers tended to play or carry out some activity I wished to photograph. I could then go to the spot most suitable for wind on that occasion, set my focus and hope for the best. Sometimes I was able, during the temporary absence of a badger, to switch on a light and alter the scale to adjust the focusing to a new spot, but that was not always possible.

At these vantage points I put in numerous nails into the trees to hang the lamp on so that I could fix it in a moment, but when no tree was available, or if I was stalking them camera in hand, I used to hang it on a button of my coat.

The easiest photographs to get are of single badgers, as you can watch them and make the exposure when they are quite still, but with two or three it is much more difficult. Large groups of badgers (if you are fortunate enough to see them) rarely give you a good opportunity when they are all comparatively motionless. Of course with an exposure of one-seventy-fifth of a second slow movement is not a disadvantage, especially if you are some distance away; but when badgers are in groups it is seldom that you find them when two or three are not playing, and then the movements are very quick and this will be very obvious on the photograph.

I always have my camera shutter set at 'ball' so that I can fire the bulb immediately after I have opened the shutter, and close it quickly again afterwards.

If I wish to get photographs at a new set, I like to go up without my camera one night to see how the badgers behave. I usually choose a vantage point about ten yards away, often standing with my back to a tree if one is available. The important thing is to see how many badgers there are when they come out, where they play, and what holes are used as exits. It is essential that your presence should not be detected on this first occasion. The next thing is to go up in the daytime a few hours before you wish to photograph them. You can then study the wind on the spot: it has a habit of coming up rides from unexpected angles and spoiling everything. Having selected my vantage point I focus the camera on the spot where I hope they will be, using my experience of watching the badgers previously to guide me.

In the evening I like to get there in good time (if it is a strange set) and get everything fitted up well before the badgers are due to emerge. It is best to approach carefully and not to go near any of the entrances. If you happen to know the direction the tunnels go, you should avoid walking above them, as vibration through the ground is easily detected and may make the badgers wary.

When the badgers emerge it is better to resist the temptation to take a photograph at once; a flash at this stage would probably put an end to the sport for the evening. If you wait, more badgers may come out, and a more interesting picture will result. You must not wait too long, however, as they may disperse to their feeding grounds and you will not get a picture at all. As soon as you think they are all out, take the photograph as quickly as possible; you usually find that they are then nearest together and a picture is more possible.

I well remember taking my first photograph at Eycot when I saw badger after badger emerge in front of me – many times I was almost pressing the shutter release, but there would be a movement, or the positions would be bad, and I would decide to wait. Eventually I had five in the field at the same time, and, concentrating on the moment when the near badgers were in a good position, I opened the shutter. That was a grand moment – a blinding flash and a stampede of badgers for the nearest hole, and a nice feeling in my bones that the photo was probably a good one.

When taking groups of the animals, certain tricks may be used to prevent movement. I have often arrested a group for a fraction of a second by clicking my tongue or giving a short whistle, but it sometimes has the opposite effect and the badgers bolt for home.

When I had taken a number of photographs of the animals near their sets, I tried to get action pictures of them doing various things. I hoped to get them scratching, digging, bringing in bedding, running, and so on. I also wanted family groups and records of the cubs as they grew up. I found this much more difficult and there are still a number of activities I wish to record which I have had no luck with so far.

Many times I have tried to get badgers bringing in their bedding, and although I have pictures I am not satisfied with them. As it is almost impossible to forecast exactly the spot from which they will get their bedding, I hit upon the idea of providing the bedding for them. The best season for this is undoubtedly autumn. I used to choose a time following several dry days. The bedding must not be handled but raked together with sticks and put on paths quite near to the set entrance. This looks quite natural as badgers often leave a bundle and collect it the following night. Several times I have had these bundles taken in by badgers, but never when I have been in the right position to photograph them. One day I hope to do it, but it is very difficult, as you can only get a good picture from certain angles.

Scratching is not a difficult activity to photograph, as badgers constantly do so outside their sets. When they are playing on their favourite tree stump they make a fine picture if you can get it, but they only do this on occasions, and if you set up your apparatus in readiness you are likely to be discovered as they rush about in all directions when excited. It was a long time before I managed to get the one illustrated, and even that shows some movement.

The great thing is to be constantly alert for any opportunity and have everything ready even if the chances are poor. In this way I was able to photograph badgers mating, and on another occasion one climbing a tree.

Close-ups of badgers coming towards you can be obtained by choosing a path leading from a set occupied by several badgers. August is a good time. You choose a place just round a corner where you can wait unseen until the badger appears. You can judge focusing distance beforehand, and take the photograph when it first appears. You usually have about a second's grace before it realizes something is wrong, assuming, of course, that the wind is in your favour.

For really good action photographs, a speed gun for synchronizing your shutter with the flash is often necessary. I have not used one myself, but I feel sure results would justify it, as you would be able to use speeds in the region of a two-fiftieth of a second.

An electrolease can successfully be used for this type of photography. The shutter and flash apparatus must be synchronized, and then you retire to the end of a long flex to fire the shutter electrically at the required moment. In my opinion this method is better left for day work, as it is often impossible to see what badgers are doing at night from any distance. A variation of this method is to use a trip-cotton. This is stretched across a badger path. When it is brushed to one side by the animal, the circuit is completed, and the shutter and flash are set off. Neither of these methods appeals to me much, as I think the real fun of the game is to be behind the camera my-self and have the thrill of seeing the animals at close quarters. What is recorded by remote control is very much a matter of chance.

Colour photography at night has its own special problems. The comparative slowness of the film necessitates the synchro-nization of several flash bulbs to get the necessary illumin-ation for an accurate exposure. Good colour rendering is de-pendent upon getting the exposure correct. In daylight it is not difficult to get the subject, foreground, and background more or less equally illuminated; thus all parts of the picture can be correctly exposed, and good colour results. But with flash bulbs operated from one direction, such as behind the camera, the light intensity quickly becomes reduced relative to the square of the distance from the light source, and even if the badger is perfectly exposed the foreground will be over-exposed and the background under-exposed; this results in false colours. I found this could be partially cured by placing the flash bulbs fairly high up so that the foreground was not over-illuminated; and, by choosing a set where there was a bank behind, there was less background to recede into the darkness.

It is necessary for this type of colour work to use colour film prepared for use with artificial light, and to use the correct filter for the flash bulbs. The gelatine filter is best inserted between the component parts of the lens of the camera.

A successful colour photograph was taken on Kodachrome B cut film from seven feet at $f/5.6$. Two large flash bulbs in reflectors were used, one on either side of the camera, one five and the other seven feet from the badger and each six feet from the ground. As correct exposure is only discovered by trial and error, these details may give some idea of the necessary illumination for this type of work.

Photographing badgers is an exciting sport, but many times have I trudged up to the woods with my apparatus, set it all up, and taken no photograph. That is inevitable, especially if you are trying to get some specific action. But when you do take something you have been working for for some time, it amply repays you for the time spent. It also lures you on to try for more and more difficult subjects, and if you fail, what matter? – badgers are grand creatures to watch, and the experience is always worth while.

CHAPTER 15

SUMMARY

Colour

THE badger's black-and-white facial coloration is in no way protective, but would appear to be aposematic; this is borne out by the general behaviour of the animal.

There are several colour variations. The silvery type is usually associated with old age, and is due to the increase in proportion of white to dark pigment in the individual hairs. No true melanic specimens have come to my notice, but some specimens approach this condition. Albinos are not extremely rare. Erythristic forms (where the black pigment is replaced by a sandy red) are not uncommon. Yellowish forms are common in some parts, the yellow replacing the white. This yellow colour may be due locally to temporary staining after a bout of digging in yellowish soil, but is more often a true hereditary characteristic. The yellowness varies very much in intensity, and observations suggest that it is controlled by multiple allelomorphs.

Distribution

Abroad, the badger is widespread throughout the greater part of Europe and Asia including Japan. Its northern limit is just south of the Arctic Circle. It is not found south of the Himalayas.

In Great Britain and Ireland they are to be found in practically every county, but are absent from the western and northern islands. In England their chief strongholds are the Peninsula counties, the Severn counties, the New Forest, the Cotswolds, Edendale, and parts of Yorkshire. They are, however, locally common in many other parts. They are rarest in East Anglia. In Scotland they are widely distributed but nowhere common. In Ireland they are found in every county but are more numerous in the south-west.

Numbers

Various methods of counting badgers were tried. The placing of sticks over set entrances was found to be unreliable during the summer when badgers constantly visited each other, but was useful at other times, and in conjunction with other methods. The visual method was the most reliable, one observer being placed near each set in the area. The presence of fresh dung in the vicinity of a set does not necessarily signify that badgers are present, though it is often a good guide.

There has been a marked increase in the numbers of badgers in the country during the past forty years. Observations in Conigre Wood showed that this increase followed a general plan of development.

The badgers' chief enemy is man. Diseased animals are seldom noticed. Accidents to badgers on railways and roads are becoming more numerous.

Food

It is certain that the badger is a truly omnivorous mammal. Its more important animal foods are all small: young mammals (especially rabbits), numerous insects (including many pests), land molluscs, and earthworms being the chief. It occasionally attacks poultry but this is by no means typical. Proved instances of lamb-killing are almost non-existent, though badgers are often blamed for this. Vegetable material forms a high proportion of the diet, especially in autumn and winter. This includes underground storage organs, fruits, nuts, and grass. There is no doubt that they do much more good than harm.

General Behaviour

Badgers have a very keen sense of smell; this is their chief sense. Hearing is also acute. The eyes are not used very much, as the more important conditioned reflexes are associated

163

with the other senses. However, badgers are quick to notice movements of any kind.

Several characteristic noises are made. The yelling sound occasionally heard is not (as was thought) connected with mating. The boar makes a 'purring' noise of sexual significance at the mating and breeding seasons when calling the sow. The squealing of the tiny cubs is soon replaced by yelping sounds when they are a little older.

Movements are very quick when alarmed, but when travelling unconcernedly, an ambling trot with frequent pauses for listening is more characteristic.

They have favourite tree-trunks on which to play, and occasionally badgers will climb trees in the manner of bears.

Bedding is brought in at regular times to line their underground chambers. Autumn is the chief season for this, but spring-cleaning and renewal of bedding is also associated with preparation for cubbing and the period when the cubs are small.

New holes or sets are usually excavated in late summer and autumn.

The time of emergence from sets is closely related to the light intensity between March and November, but in winter is more unpredictable. Shortness of the night in mid-summer brings them out earlier, and so does warmth. Strong moonlight may deter them from emerging.

Hibernation

Conclusive evidence has been obtained that badgers do not hibernate in the south of England. It is probable that they do not do so anywhere in Great Britain. In Central and Eastern Europe they spend certain periods in a state of hibernation, but emerge during warmer spells even in Russia and parts of Siberia.

Activity is certainly reduced during December and January in this country, but only under exceptional conditions will they remain underground for more than a few days at a time.

Musk-glands

Evidence has been collected that these glands are used as a result of fear or excitement. The sudden recognition of danger will cause the secretion, and so will the excitement of prolonged and boisterous play. It has also been noted during play which has a sexual significance, and prior to copulation.

Reproductive Cycle

The normal time for cubs to be born in the south of England is February and the average number between two and three.

Sufficient evidence has been obtained that the mating season is July and early August, though it may possibly extend into September. The sexual urge in the female may start waning in August. Mating takes place when the cubs are still with the parents, suggesting that they pair for life. A sow normally has cubs each year.

During August and part of September there appears to be a tendency for several families to live together in one large set while the other sets are spring-cleaned ready for the winter.

Cubs leave their parents during late September or early October.

Development

After fertilization the blastocyst does not become embedded in the uterine wall for about five months. During this unattached stage growth hardly takes place at all. Implantation occurs during December or early January and then development is rapid, the young being born eight weeks after implantation. Gestation is thus seven months.

Abnormally long gestations are not uncommon in captive animals, and it seems likely that this is due to implantation being delayed beyond the five months.

Sets

Badgers are very adaptable in making sets in all kinds of country and soils, though woodland is the most typical habitat.

They are usually excavated in the vicinity of water and on sloping land. Some sets penetrate to a distance of one hundred yards into a hillside, and others form a labyrinth of tunnels three storeys deep. Ancient sets in woodland often have a typical flora (of nettles and elders) surrounding them. Foxes, rabbits, and rats are not unusually found along with badgers in the larger sets.

APPENDIX I

THE following time has been spent by the author on observation work on badgers:

In Conigre Wood:	111 visits in the daytime totalling	84 hours
In Conigre Wood:	105 visits at night totalling	197 hours
In other parts of Glos., ⎧	50 visits in daytime totalling	20 hours
Somerset, and Wilts. ⎩	25 visits at night totalling	40 hours
Totals:	290 visits	341 hours

Most of the work in Conigre Wood was carried out between June 1943 and December 1945, the work in Somerset during 1946–7.

The following is a summary of a short period of observation work carried out when the cubs were above ground for the first few times:

26 April 1945	Night	A, B	2 hours	2 adults and 2 cubs seen at A. At least 2 seen at B. Put sticks over C, D, and E before leaving.
27 ,, ,,	Day	All	1 hour	General observations at all sets. Signs of bedding, dung, activity. Sticks over D and E not moved, but those at C moved.
27 ,, ,,	Night	A, B	2 hours	Sow and 2 cubs at A. Others seen at B. Photographed one cub at A.
28 ,, ,,	Day	All	¾ hour	General observations. New hole excavated at A, making 5 in all.
30 ,, ,,	Night	A	1¾ hours	2 adults and 2 cubs at A. Some heard at B.
1 May ,,	Night	A, B	2 hours	2 adults and 2 cubs at A, 3 adults and 4 cubs at B (Groves). Erythristic cubs and mother seen for first time. Sticks unmoved at C.
3 ,, ,,	Night	B	2 hours	Saw adults but no cubs, but I heard the latter below ground.
4 ,, ,,	Night	B, A	2 hours	No sign at B, heard nothing at A. Later, went to C where there were signs of occupation.
6 ,, ,,	Night	C	2 hours	Saw the family previously seen at A – 2 adults and 2 cubs. Sticks put over A the night before were not moved.

8 May 1945	Day	All	¾ hour	General observations. Fresh dung at E.
10 ,, ,,	Day	All	¾ hour	Evidence that A is occupied again, E probably used. D certainly not.
12 ,, ,,	Night	All	2½ hours	Full count with boys at each set. 2 adults and 2 cubs at A. 1 adult and 2 cubs at B. None seen at C, D, or E, but noises may have interfered.
16 ,, ,,	Night	B	2 hours	Saw 2 adults and 2 cubs at B. Activity heard at A, where there was obviously a family.

The above is typical of the type of work carried out over the intensive period. Details have not been included in this summary.

APPENDIX II

Date		Time (G.M.T.)	Locality	Comments
5 Feb.	1945	6.45	Rendcomb	
17 Feb.	1945	6.45	,,	
20 Feb.	1945	6.35	,,	
24 Feb.	1945	6.40	,,	
27 Feb.	1945	7.25	,,	
1 March	1945	7.25	,,	
8 March	1945	7.40	,,	
11 March	1945	7.30	,,	
17 March	1945	7.30	,,	
23 March	1945	8.45	,,	Very bright moonlight
26 March	1945	8.35	,,	Very bright moonlight
3 April	1945	7.40	,,	Dark night
4 April	1945	7.40	,,	Dark night
5 April	1945	8.10	,,	Much lighter
11 April	1945	7.45	,,	Very warm, no moon
14 April	1945	7.45	Warminster	Very hot
23 April	1944	8.10	Rendcomb	
24 April	1946	8.20	Nr. Taunton	
26 April	1945	8.10	Rendcomb	
30 April	1945	8.10	,,	
1 May	1945	8.20	,,	
6 May	1945	8.30	,,	
8 May	1944	8.10	,,	
20 May	1944	8.25	,,	
24 May	1944	8.20	,,	
6 June	1945	8.15	,,	
7 June	1945	8.30	,,	
12 June	1945	8.30	,,	
20 June	1945	8.30	,,	
21 June	1945	8.45	,,	
22 June	1944	8.25	,,	
26 June	1944	8.30	,,	

TIME OF EMERGENCE FROM SETS (*continued*)

Date		Time (G.M.T.)	Locality	Comments
10 July	1945	8.30	Rendcomb	
17 July	1945	8.30	,,	
20 July	1945	8.15	,,	
21 July	1945	8.30	,,	
1 Aug.	1945	8.05	,,	
4 Aug.	1944	7.55	,,	Very hot
8 Aug.	1944	7.55	,,	
15 Aug.	1944	7.55	,,	
23 Aug.	1945	8.05	,,	
25 Aug.	1944	7.35	,,	
25 Aug.	1945	7.30	,,	
30 Aug.	1946	7.30	Nr. Taunton	
8 Sept.	1945	7.00	Rendcomb	
13 Sept.	1947	7.05	Nr. Taunton	
17 Sept.	1946	6.45	,,	
20 Sept.	1944	6.40	Rendcomb	
22 Sept.	1945	6.40	,,	
26 Sept.	1945	6.40	,,	
3 Oct.	1945	6.25	,,	
8 Oct.	1945	6.30	,,	
13 Oct.	1945	6.45	,,	
15 Oct.	1946	6.30	Nr. Taunton	
16 Oct.	1944	6.10	Rendcomb	
17 Oct.	1946	6.45	Nr. Taunton	
19 Oct.	1945	6.10	Rendcomb	
27 Oct.	1945	6.15	,,	
1 Nov.	1945	5.55	,,	
4 Nov.	1945	6.00	,,	
6 Nov.	1945	5.45	,,	
14 Nov.	1945	5.40	,,	
12 Dec.	1945	5.45	,,	

(Compare with graph on p. 97.)

APPENDIX III

INHERITED characters are passed on to the next generation as a result of genes or factors which are present in the chromosomes of the nucleus of both egg and sperm. The fertilized egg receives one set of chromosomes from each parent. If each parent is pure-bred for a character, such as colour, it follows that the fertilized egg will contain a pair of similar colour genes, one on the chromosome passed on by the sperm, and the other on the corresponding chromosome passed on by the egg. If, however, one parent is pure-bred for black colour and the other is pure-bred for white, the fertilized egg will receive a gene producing blackness on one chromosome, and a gene producing whiteness on the corresponding one. These contrasting factors, black and white, are said to form a pair of allelomorphs. Usually, the next generation is either white or black. The colour which is visible is called the dominant, and the other is the recessive. The recessive is not lost but only hidden. Thus many inherited characters are influenced by a single pair of allelomorphs.

In the above example we have considered the genes as completely independent entities, but this is not always the case, as they can sometimes reinforce each other. Thus it is possible to have a series of genes which act together to intensify an effect. These series are known as multiple allelomorphs. For example, there are series of multiple allelomorphs determining fur colour in various mammals, in which the effects produced form a graded series. I believe a similar condition occurs in the badger. In all these series, the intermediates are common and the extremes rare. Thus, if four allelomorphic pairs are involved, there would only be one chance in two hundred and fifty-six of one of the extremes appearing: hence the unusualness of the very yellow badger seen in Conigre Wood.

BIBLIOGRAPHY

BAKER, F.J. (1908). *The Victoria History of the County of Kent.* London, Constable. *1*: 304.

BATTEN, H.M. (1923). *The Badger Afield and Underground.* London, Witherby.

  (1925). Habits and Economics of the Badger. *J. Minist. Agric. 32*: 572–7.

BEDDARD, F.E. (1923). *The Mammalia. Cambridge Natural History.* London, Macmillan.

BOBRINSKII, N. A., KUZELZOV, B. A., and KUZYAKIN, A. P. (1944). Key to the Mammals of the U.S.S.R. State Publishing House *Soviet Science*, Moscow. 132.

BONOMI, A. (1901). Il Tasso (*Meles taxus*) nel Trentino. *Boll. Soc. Zool. Ital.* ser. 2, 2: 41.

BUCKNILL, J.A. (1902). *The Victoria History of the County of Surrey.* London, Constable. *1*: 222.

BUTTERWORTH, W. C. J. R. (1905). *The Victoria History of the County of Sussex.* London, Constable. *1*: 303.

CAMBELL, C. (1897). Badger Colony in Dalmery Park. *Trans. Edinb. Field Nat. Micro. Soc. 3*: 232–6.

CHEESEMAN, L.E. (1920). The Home Life of Badgers. *Proc. Croydon Nat. Sci. Soc. 9*: 29–37.

CLARK, J. (1906). *The Victoria History of the County of Cornwall.* London, Constable. *1*: 350.

COCKS, J.A. (1903–4). Gestation of the Badger. *Zoologist*, ser. 4, 7: 441–3; *8*: 108–14.

DARLING, F.F. (1947). *Natural History in the Highlands and Islands. New Naturalist Series.* London, Collins.

DAVIES, G. (1936). Distribution of the Badger in Denbigh, and Notes on Breeding and Other Habits. *J. Anim. Ecol. 5*: 97–104.

DENT, G. (1922). Badgers in Essex. *Essex Nat. 20*: 108.

DICKINSON, W. (1875). *Cumbriana.* London. 172.

E—., A. (1903). Badgers Breeding Above Ground. *Field, 101*: 573.

ELTON, C. (1929). *The Victoria History of the County of Oxford.* London, Oxford University Press. *1*: 219.

FAIRFAX-BLAKEBOROUGH, J., and PEASE, A. E. (1914). The Life and Habits of the Badger. London, *The Foxhound.*

FISCHER, E. (1931). Early stages in Embryology of the Badger. *Verh. Anat. Ges. Jena, 40*: 22–34.

BIBLIOGRAPHY

FORREST, H. E. (1907). *The Fauna of North Wales.* London, Witherby.

GRAHAM, R. (1946). The Badger in Cumberland. *Trans. Carlisle Nat. Hist. Soc.* 7: 88–99.

HAMILTON, W. I. (1939). *American Mammals.* New York, McGraw-Hill. 223–38.

HARDY, E. (1944). The Badger. *Discovery,* 5: 314–15.

HARTING, J.E. (1888). The Badger. *Zoologist,* ser. 3, 12: 3.

HARVIE-BROWN, J.A. (1882). The Past and Present Distribution of some of the Rarer Animals of Scotland. *Zoologist,* ser. 3, 6: 2.

HATFIELD, J. (1942). Mammals of Central Arizona. *Bull. Chicago Acad. Sci.* 6: 143–57.

KING, H.H. (1931). Working Terriers, Badgers and Badger Digging. London, *The Field.*

LANGUM, F.H. (1945). Wild Animals and Agriculture. *J. Minist. Agric.* 52: 31–4.

LEACH, E.F. (1901). Some notes on Badgers. *J. Northants. Nat. Hist. Soc.* 11: 107–11.

LÖNNBERG, E. (1928). Contributions to the Biology and Morphology of the Badger and some other Carnivora. *Ark. Zool. Stockholm,* 19, No. 26: 1–11.

MACPHERSON, H.A. (1901). *The Victoria History of the County of Cumberland.* London, Constable. 1: 221.

MEADE-WALDO, E.G. (1894). The Badger: its Period of Gestation. *Zoologist,* ser. 3, 18: 221.

MIDDLETON, A.D. (1935). *Meles meles*: Food from Stomach Examination. *J. Anim. Ecol.* 4: 274.

MILLAIS, J.G. (1904). *Mammals of Great Britain.* London, Longmans, Green. 2: 37–70.

MITCHELL, P. C. (1912). *The Childhood of Animals.* London, Heinemann.

MOFFATT, C.B. (1927). *Meles taxus* in Ireland. *Irish Nat.* 1: 130–2

NICHOLAS, M. (1946). Watching Badgers. *Countrygoer,* 5: 28–32.

OGNEV, S.I. (1931). *The Mammals of Eastern Europe and Northern Asia,* Moscow and Leningrad. Vol. 2.

OWEN, R. (1846). *A History of British Fossil Mammals and Birds.* London. 109–11.

PARKER, T.H. (1941). The Badger. *Naturalist, 1941*: 141–5.

PATERSON, J. (1904). The Gestation of the Badger. *Zoologist,* ser. 3, 18: 108–11.

PATTERSON, A.J. (1908). The Badger in Norfolk. *Zoologist*, ser. 4, *12*: 426–7.

PEASE, SIR A. (1895). *The Badger*. London, Lawrence & Bullen.

PITT, F. (1933). Habits and Status of the Badger in Britain. *J. Soc. Preserv. Faun. Empire*, *no. 18*: 15–19.

  (1935). Recent Increases in Badger Population in Shropshire and Great Britain. *J. Anim. Ecol. 4*: 1–6.

  (1945). *Wild Animals in Britain*. London, Batsford, 23–9.

  (1941). *Meles meles :* Present Status and Future Chances of Survival. *J. Soc. Preserv. Faun. Empire, no. 42*: 17–21.

POCOCK, R.I. (1911). Some Probable and Possible Instances of Warning Characteristics amongst Insectivorous and Carnivorous Mammals. *Ann. Mag. Nat. Hist. 8*: 750–7.

  (1940). *Arctonyx collaris*, Consul. Sub-species in Burma. *Proc. Bombay Nat. Hist. Soc. 41* : 465.

PRELL, H. (1930). Period of Gestation in Mustelids. *Zool. Anz. Leipzig, 87* : 273–83.

RUSSELL, H. (1913). *The Flea*. London, Cambridge University Press.

SETON, E.T. (1910). *Life Histories of Northern Mammals*. London, Constable. 995–1009.

SIMPSON, C.G. (1945). The Principles of Classification and a Classification of Mammals. New York, *Bull. Amer. Mus. Nat. Hist. 85*: 114.

SWAYNE, R.A. (1908). *The Victoria History of the County of Hereford*. London, Constable. *1* : 153.

TAMS, R.F. (1904). *The Victoria History of the County of Warwickshire*, London, Constable.

TETLEY, H.E. (1940). The Land Mammals of the Bristol District. *Proc. Bristol Nat. Soc.* ser. 4, *9* : 140–1.

THOMPSON, A.R. (1931). *Nature by Night*. London, Ivor Nicholson & Watson.

TREGARTHEN, J.C. (1925). *The Badger*. London, Murray.

  (1931). The Badger in West Cornwall. *J. Roy. Instn. Cornwall, 23* : 256–64.

VESEY-FITZGERALD, B. (1942). *A County Chronicle*. London, Chapman & Hall. 126–33.

VOGT, C. (1887). *The Mammalia*. London. Blackie. *1* : 213–6.

WHITE, T.D. (1903). After Badger. *Badminton Magazine, 17* : 69.

INDEX